Ben

The Ministry Of Silly Hats

Or,

Doctor, Will I be able to Play the Guitar
After my Treatment?

Published By

Wine Press,
1 Silver Street,
Tamworth,
Staffordshire, B79 7NH
Tel: 01827 67622

ISBN 1 86237 071 0

To all those people I forgot to mention
in this text...

Introduction

This is my attempt to get some of my thoughts into a permanent form. It is something I have wanted to do for a while. I have nearly written a book on a number of occasions. Now I have a motive so to do.

I am terminally ill with Cancer. That seems to me a fairly good reason to try to do something that will outlast me. My aim is that a few people will read this and what I say will connect with their experience. I hope at the very least they will go away and think a bit more about life and what a strange thing it is.

I reckon that as people go, I have seen quite a lot of life in a pretty short space of time, and this is my way of trying to pass on some of my experiences and thoughts that have occurred to me over my brief time on this stage. I've been around now for nearly nineteen years. I don't know how long I've been given, but that's no different from anyone else on this planet. I have, however, tried to fill my life, and I think I've done OK, though I say so myself. Everyone is given the same - a lifetime - and mine's been full. This thought came from one of Neil Gaiman's books. He is a sharp bloke, and I recommend to anyone his graphic novels (which is a grownup euphemism for comic) about the Sandman, in particular the one about Death. (Death the anthropomorphic personification, not death the event)

This book is about my experiences of my life and my illness, the way in which this has affected and shaped the way I look at the world, and some of my observations about people, and the way in which they behave, and what makes them tick. Human beings are highly peculiar, and I love the way they are so utterly unique. I hope that you find it interesting and maybe even thought provoking, but I am not going to get my hopes up. I'll settle for you finishing it, that in itself is a compliment.

Chapter 1 - The Beginning

I was born on the twelfth of July 1978, in an insignificant corner of a ward in the maternity suite of the now closed Groundslow Hospital, which is (just about) in Stoke-On-Trent. As it happens, my dad moved house while my mum was in hospital having me. I reckon he was trying to lose her. Unfortunately for his little plan, she caught up with him, and I was taken home to a nice house in Gnosall, which is a small village in Staffordshire. Apparently, my dad had only just got a driving license, and my mum claims that the reason for this is that the nurses on the ward where I was born wouldn't let him take her (and me) home on the back of his motorbike. I have never decided whether I believe my parents about these tales, but they make good stories. I remember absolutely nothing about Gnosall, as I was very small.

Shortly afterwards, we moved to Leek. We lived in a small house in Leek which is a small town in the Staffordshire Moorlands, not far from Stoke-On-Trent. My earliest memory of Leek is falling down the stairs. It is a significant comment on the human condition that most peoples earliest memory is something like this. We remember it because of pain. Some clever people can probably draw deep and meaningful conclusions from that, but personally, I am a pragmatist, and I think it's because it hurt.

Actually, we had really cool stairs in Leek, at least from the point of view of a toddler. They were wooden, with slatted steps, and they went round a corner. I (apparently, I don't remember this) used to sit under them and peek out through the steps. I remember the corner in them, as that is where I landed when I fell down. Had the corner not been there, I'd have gone the full distance.

I had a fun childhood, doing all the sorts of fun childhood things that people read about in books, and think 'I wish I had done things like that'. I don't know whether its just me, or whether I was lucky and had the opportunity, but I went and did them. I hope that most kids get to do the sorts of things that I did, but I fear that the advent of technology and a lot of other small social changes between the time when I was small - the first half of the eighties - and now - the late nineties - have changed things. I have a closer outlook and experience of childhood to my parents, a good twenty-something years before me, than to my siblings, a mere four (and eight and ten) years after me. What this really says is that the way kids play, and the sorts of things that they do, and the experience of things that they have has changed more in the last five-ten years than in the previous twenty. That's worrying, don't you think?

I did all sorts of fun things. Building tree houses, exploring haunted cellars, swiping apples, bridging and damning bab-bling brooks, running away fairly regularly, building igloos in winter, sliding on ice, snowball fights, sledging, Christmas (white, obviously) etc. etc. etc. I had great childhood friends, that I now have no contact with. I slept over at friends houses, went home with them for tea occasionally, and so on. I had a proper childhood, not the pretend plastic sort consisting of an endless round of TV, and assorted neon-coloured commercial toys.

For example, not so very long ago, I was talking with my

8

sister about making slides in the playground at primary school by compacting snow into ice, so you could slide from one end of the playground to the other. I hope at this point that you are thinking, 'Yes, I remember doing that'. My sister, who is eight years younger than me, didn't know what I was on about. I couldn't believe it. She had no idea about this concept, and had never heard of it. A great childhood experience had been lost. Oh, sure, many people object on grounds of danger, and the sport has been outlawed in schools due to a proliferation of broken legs and so on, but then it wasn't allowed in our school either, a decade ago. That didn't stop us doing it, and the fact that ten years on, the kids don't even know that the activity exists due to the draconian methods of making sure they don't do it says something very worrying. The systematic banning of activities that are deemed dangerous only serves to promote ignorance and reinforce stereotype and prejudice, while at the same time reducing the breadth of experience that people have. What is worse is that after a while, the ideas that have been banned cease to exist in the culture of the school kids, and as a result, it becomes no longer necessary to ban the activity, as it simply ceases to exist, permanently erased from the culture it was born of. This may be an extreme way of stating the case for something like sliding in the snow, but the logic is scalable to other problems and situations. A different example - a huge proportion of under tens won't ever have held a match, much less struck one. That's very scary. What happens when twenty years on they want to build a bonfire in the garden? OK, by then it will be illegal anyway due to the potential environmental harm, but that's by the by. They won't be safe to do so, as they will never have had experience of handling fire. Wrapping people in cotton wool so they never experience 'dangerous' things is denying them the right to many pastimes and activities that bring great good. People need sound education, to experience responsibility, and a pragmatic and sensible approach to dealing with problems and potential danger. A simple ban will also have the knock on effect that such activities are then lost to the cultural memory permanently. Part of learning responsibility and the value of things is getting burnt occasionally. Experience is something you only get just after you need it.

I read voraciously, and tried to use what I read. I would get hold of ancient books on esoteric subjects, then go out and try to use the information. I read one on how to make bows and arrows, the technical differences between bow designs, and so on. I then went out into the fields and made a bow by picking the right tree, and binding and lashing branches to form a bow with the correct strength variation along its length. I loved the technical side of things. I boned up on electrical things, and found out about computers. I was lucky enough to be around and the right age when home computers really took off, and I had an Acorn Electron to play with. I taught myself to program. Unfortunately, it's not (and wasn't then) cool to be enthusiastic at things. I came to much grief among my peers at primary school, because I was interested in things, the sorts of things that they weren't. I believe that all people should be interested in something, and should do something. My interests are academic and centred on computing and maths, but other peoples interests are and should be different, and they should be pursued. Personal education in your own interests should be fuelled from your own enthusiasm. Instilling that thirst is what school should be about. We need to provide the platter of experience to chose our interests from. If people don't have the opportunity to experience what is on offer in terms of their own potential interests, to find out what the world can offer them, then they will never discover any hobbies or interests, and they become doomed to lead a life of watching cheap Australian soap operas and crap game shows. There must be thousands of

10

people who could be great wood turners or chefs or rock climbers or interior designers if they had been given (or, dare I say it had it forced upon them in school) the opportunity to try it.

I was lucky...

Chapter 2 - The Scholarship

My grandmother started it, by finding the advert in the paper. She passed it on to my mum and dad, and they asked me. It was about a scheme run by Eton College, to try to get some people who would otherwise not be able to go, to go to the school. The scheme was called the Junior Scholarship, and the deal was this: Eton awarded a few places to those it chose from an examination-and-interview process. The qualification for entry was having been educated in the state system for the previous three years.

At the time it was explained in simple terms to me. I was, at the time of the exam, nine, nearly ten. I took it, needless to say. There were three exams, a Maths test, an English test, and an Intelligence test, carefully designed to measure aptitude, not the amount of things you had crammed. I did reasonably well, I think, or at least well enough to be one of the three asked back for interview.

It was while we were being shown around, a guided tour, with all the junior scholarship candidates and parents, that I first met Mrs Anderson, the wife of the then headmaster. There was this crowd of parents and kids being shown round, with Mrs A at the head, and me, skipping along beside her, asking question after question after question. My parents were at the back, wondering where I had got to. All was fine, till I started to proclaim in a loud voice, 'Mum, the Guide says this...' and 'the Guide says that' and so on, and of course my mum curled up in shame and at the first opportunity, grabbed me and hissed 'That's not the Guide, that is the headmasters wife! Shut UP!'

All of which was rather over my head.

Much of the significance of 'Eton' as an institution and what it was and the position it holds was way over my head at the time. As far as I was concerned it was just another school, with the added complication of sleeping there too. I am still not sure why the idea appealed to me.

I had my interviews, I don't remember much about them now, apart from animatedly explaining to one of the teachers the inner workings of a nuclear power station, which I was terribly proud of knowing, as I had read all about it the previous week. I thought this was great knowledge, as there couldn't be that many people who knew. After all, no-one had ever told me that they knew, and if they did, they would have, as it was such a cool thing to know.

They gave me the place. My mum went nuts, and wouldn't stop jumping up and down for a week. I was quite happy, too.

Before I could go to Eton, which took people at thirteen, I had to go to a prep school for three years, which was also catered for under the terms of the scholarship, to catch up on the rest of the people in the public school system, who were significantly further along in terms of what they knew than I was. For a start, they had done a years Latin and French.

I think that people should start to learn as much as they can as soon as they can, to get into the habit. Picking up French and Latin at ten is a lot easier than starting it two years later. Starting at nine, or even eight as in some peoples cases I knew, makes life so much easier, and a bit of mockery of the GCSE. In my year at Eton, eleven people got B's at French GCSE. The

13

rest, (two hundred and thirty-ish) got A's. And we took the exam a year early. OK, there is the effect of selection to take into account, and there is a basic minimum intelligence at Eton, but I think to a large part, having done French for a year or two longer than the rest of the country is what makes the difference. This applies in other subjects. At nine, children soak up information. Getting them started by loading them up with lots to find out about, and working them hard and giving them a wide range of fodder for the mind will enable them to find something which lights a spark. They will grumble wildly at having to do all this work that for the most part they are not interested in but they will find something, if the range of food is wide enough, that they like, and they can then pursue that.

My prep school, Packwood, did that for me. I had some great teachers, and some crap ones. But the damage was done. I was shown that there are more things to find out about than I had believed possible, and I had competition in finding out about them. The quality of teachers is another vital factor in the quality of schooling. My teachers taught a lesson. We were sat in rows, alphabetically, usually, and the teacher was up at the front, using a blackboard (and later whiteboard) to set out the information and teach it. This requires forward planning, enthusiasm for the subject matter, and presentation skills from the teacher. He/she must be actively teaching, as children do not absorb information by osmosis. This is far more demanding of the teacher than the wishy-washy arrange-the-pupils-in-groups-round-circular-tables-and-let-them-work-it-out-for-themselves approach that seems to be prevalent now. Whole class teaching works better. It is the difference between an active sales push, from sales personnel in a store, and letting a customer browse the shelves aimlessly.

A good teacher, and as I said, I was lucky to have them,

14

expects their pupils to do well, and expects excellence. I hear cries of 'but not everyone is clever, not everyone can achieve excellence'. Yes they can. They can reach the top of their personal tree, they can do as well as they can. They should not be taught to the lowest common denominator, or even the average of the class. Time should be made for each pupil, and they should each be stretched to find their own personal limits. 'But that creates resentment and feelings of inadequacy among the less bright' Stream the pupils. The world is by nature competitive. Getting people used to competition, and pushing them to exceed their own expectations of themselves will serve to get them used to trying, and get them used to failure, too. If someone who is bright comes through a school system never having been stretched or tested, always having been able to run rings around everyone, then they will come slap bang up against the brick wall of not being the best sooner or later with no experience of how to deal with it. I learnt at Packwood. It was kinder to do that in school than in the real world.

I had real competition at Packwood. I wasn't the best, in fact almost everyone else had a major head start on me in terms of material covered. They also had two years experience of living away from home and they knew the ground rules, and the way things worked. They knew how not to make a complete fool of themselves in public, and when to back down gracefully. Which is more than I did.

I caught up, though. In may have been a sink or swim thing, but eventually I realised that the reason I was having the trouble was me, not them, and if I insisted on making a total idiot of myself, then I deserved everything I got.

I had some problems, though. One example was bed time routine. There was a rota system, everyone was assigned two bath nights a week, and they were expected to turn up for them on the right night, and have one. I simply didn't know about this, and as a result had a bath every night when I felt like it. The matron caught on to this, when I had had one four nights in a row, and asked, hang on a minute, hadn't she seen me rather a lot this week? I said yes, why? Was there a problem? Ten minutes later the system was rather clearly explained, and from then on I played by it. This was a minor thing, but it shows the kind of problems I had in a group of people who all knew the ground rules.

Another example was in my first lesson. I did not know that the custom was to stand up when an adult (i.e. My teacher) entered the room. This was a totally new concept to me, having come fresh from the state system. Consequently, when the teacher came in, everyone except me leapt up bolt upright, and I stayed calmly sitting in my place, and I got a huge bawling out from said teacher. It wasn't my fault I didn't know, since this was simply completely outside my experience. The guy should have realised this, of course, but then he wasn't a great teacher at the best of times.

I did have some brilliant teachers. One was a middle aged gentleman called Mr Roe. He was the deputy head, and in the best tradition of deputy heads, had scary eyebrows. This man was a brilliant teacher. He was imaginative, funny, dedicated, and good at his subject. He was the one that got me interested in maths, and taught me the most important foundation blocks that most of the rest of maths is based on.

An example: When he taught us trigonometry, we did the usual gubbins involving triangles and trees and angles and things, then he hired a theodolite, and proceeded out onto the playing fields and we measured the height of the trees. Then we practised surveying, and figured out how much further the people on the outside of the running track had to run, and

16

finally, as a piece de resistance we piled into the back of his ancient and creaking landrover, and chugged off up to the local trig point, and checked the information on the OS map as to the size of the school by triangulation. The map was even right.

That's a lot more interesting than some conventional ways of being taught trig.

He also used to do grounds maintenance around the school. On Wednesday afternoons, he'd pickup a load of pupils who weren't in teams, and again, we'd pile into the landrover, and chug off down to the Spinney. The Spinney was a small section of forest down by the river at the bottom end of the school grounds. Most people spent most of their Sunday afternoons playing down there. It was good fun. I built a stonking treehouse once... but I digress. On one occasion I remember Mr Roe pulled up along side a bramble and bracken infested slope and doled out scythes. Then he simply said to go and clear it. The blackberries were out, as I remember, and we had a whale of a time just slashing and cutting, and stuffing ourselves with berries. All afternoon.

The Lego Technic Club was also run by him, and he used to set the group of about a half dozen boys a challenge, like 'Build a vehicle capable of climbing over a pile of three maths textbooks under its own power' or simply 'Build a six foot span bridge'. This last was a great challenge, and we finally persuaded him that we could be allowed to use string, and built a six foot span suspension bridge between two desks in his classroom. It stayed there for a week, and was proudly shown off to all members of the school who saw it.

Packwood was an amazing place, but it underwent a subtle change in the culture while I was there. (And that is not due to the fact that I was there, either!) The term that I arrived was the same term that a new headmaster arrived. The old head, a certain Mr Pease-Watkin was a real character, the sort of traditional headmaster that is beyond stereotype. The new head had a totally different style and emphasis. I did not know Mr Pease-Watkin, but my parents describe the difference between the two men very accurately by not describing them at all. They describe their offices. Naturally they were the same room, but one was when Mr Pease-Watkin initially met my parents, and the other is after the new head had taken over, when he met them for some now forgotten reason. This account is second hand, from what I remember of a conversation with my mum.

Mr Pease-Watkin's secretary escorted my mum and dad into the office, where upon every surface, floor space, and anywhere else that they could be perched were piles of paper, and books. She dashed about, embarrassedly throwing piles of stuff off the chairs onto the floor, and offered my parents a rather tattered seat. She said word to the effect that he would arrive shortly, and there would be tea and biscuits along in a minute. The office was a jumbled heap of education paraphernalia. There were cricket bats and bails and books and Latin papers and pens and work and books and reports and letters and post coming in and books and stuff concerned with holidays and big jars of sweets behind the desk and books and teaching hours and filing cabinets and books, and oh yes, I remember, some more books.

The new heads office, the same room, gleamed. It shone. It was neat and tidy, and not a thing out of place. There was a nice tidy bookshelf with nice tidy books, and a comfy settee, and a glass topped coffee table with a couple of smart magazines on, and his desk, which had a (you guessed it) neat and tidy pile of A4 on it.

18

Mr Pease-Watkin had really lived for the school. He had had a traditional, classical approach to running the school. The most important things to him were the schools success at sporting fixtures and its Common Entrance results. He was interested in the people, and worked for those who were there, and as a result, the school had gained a reputation for excellence. The new head had a very modern approach. He revamped the prospectus and magazine, and tried to up the reputation of the school by marketing. He increased the sales pitch to new parents, and advertised the school on the grounds of the physical facilities available. This culture change slowly filtered out over into the school.

The school may have mourned the retirement of PW, but there were plenty of characters left around the school. Some of the other masters were equally eccentric. Most had suitably disrespectful nicknames. I should point out here that it is a high mark of honour to have a nickname. It meant you were interesting enough to bother with. Those masters who did not have one were merely boring. Those who did fell into two categories. Those you took the piss out of because you did not respect them, and those you took the piss from because you did respect them.

For instance, Boffer was a Latin teacher who simply failed to understand that people deliberately wound him up because he rose so easily, and to our 11 year old eyes, looked bloody silly when he shouted, as had a strange habit of sucking in his lower lip so he looked like he had no teeth.

The Rabbi, on the other hand, was respected. Mind, it is a bit difficult to have anything but respect for a man who is six foot seven, and plays rugby. Lots. He had a whopper nose, and taught Science. He was cool. I remember once, when we were 'doing' lungs, and respiration in mammals more generally, he

19

got hold of some pigs lungs and proceeded to attach a bit of rubber pipe to the trachea, so he could blow them up. He did, and we oohed, and ahhed, and then he released the pressure. Of course, a stream of mucus and blood from inside the lungs proceeded to spray all over his head and face, and in his hair etc., as the lungs deflated and the rubber tube acted as a nozzle. We were rolling in the aisles. We got the rest of the lesson off, while he went and had a very thorough shower.

Another rather eccentric character was a certain Mr Baker, who taught French. I got on well with him. In his spare time, he organised the outdoor pursuits efforts of the school. It was through him that I was introduced to most of the sports that I really took to. Amongst other things, like orienteering and canoeing, we did a lot of hill walking. A couple of times a term, he would get a list of enthusiasts, and we would pack up and head off to Snowdonia. It was his ambition to do all of the Welsh Munroes (i.e. all the peaks in wales that top 3000 feet) within a school year. I did most of them, I think. I was certainly on the list to go every time, but the demand was great and the places limited. To date, I think I have done all but three.

I loved the walks. We would do three or four peaks in a day, to make it worthwhile, and then come back to school, exhausted but satisfied. Some of the best moments that stand out were things like the time we rose right above the clouds, to see Wales spread out below us as nothing but a series of peaks breaking an endless sea of cloud. I remember snowball fights in June on Carrnedd Llewellen, and sledging on our Waterproofs, damning the stream that led through the campsite at four am when everyone woke up, sleeping in a cow barn that a farmer lent us, and many others that are too numerous to mention.

The best trip I had was one of the last, though. We were short a couple of peaks for our target of finishing all 15 that we needed to do in the year, so a last ditch attempt was staged. Mr Baker, me, and another friend called Binkle, (I still can't remember his real name) piled into the man's trusty blue Mini Cooper, and off we went.

We got to where we were going at about five pm, and set off up the mountain. We needed to 'bag' Elidir Fawr and another of the Glyders whose name escapes me. We did it, and watched the sunset down the Nan Ffrancon valley as we sat on the top. We came down in the dark, which was very cool indeed, and set up camp behind a dry stone wall not far from the A5, made a cup of Hot Chocolate, and got into our bivi bags sometime after midnight.

The next morning, I had my breakfast sitting on a Roman arch bridge over a mountain stream, which is actually underneath the real modern A5 road bridge. We piled back into the mini, and drove round the mountain into the next valley to meet the rest of our class who were joining us to do the last three peaks that we needed, the three that make up the Snowdon Horseshoe.

Most of the group went up the Pyg track, which is a relatively good path that winds its way up the inside of the horseshoe to the summit of Snowdon itself, but we, in our role as hard-core explorers, needed to go around the top of the horseshoe, to do the required peaks. This included Crib Goch. You will probably have heard of Striding Edge, as being a bit of serious ridge. Crib Goch is the Welsh equivalent, and to my mind it is a lot worse. It is a mile or so long, and a totally sheer edge, that drops away to the valley floor a long way away on either side.

We worked our way along it, and all was going well, we

were staggering, one foot on either side, on the slope, like walking on a barn roof, when we met a big party of school age children having a rest. This wasn't a problem, as we negotiated our way around them, but it was there that we saw the Game Boy boy. This was a lad, sitting on a rock in one of the most fantastic places in this fair island. On a thousand foot sheer ridge that is itself three thousand feet above sea level, on a day with exceptional weather when we could see most of Snowdonia. He was hunched, playing a Game Boy, with headphones on, intently concentrating on the beeps and ker-chings coming from it. In a way, I felt sorry for him. He was so wrapped up in his world of Mario that he was blind to the view, blind to the effort and planning and sheer hard work that was put into organising the trip for him. He had his fingers in his ears and his eyes screwed shut, in case the real world came along and bit him. It was his loss.

Duly, we got around to Snowdon, and fittingly completed our journey, and the last summit. We were happy as a group, but personally, I did not like Snowdon. There is a basic problem with it. It is commercial. It is the biggest, and therefore is the spoilt one. I far prefer the top of Carrnedd Llewellen, which is a mere fifty feet lower, as it is quiet, and all you can see is the occasional equally reverential walker. You are left to appreciate the majesty of the mountain without being enticed to buy a cheap plastic memento. (By the way, the name, Carrnedd Llewellen, is Welsh for something along the lines of 'Llewellen's great big pile of stones' which I think is an excellent name for a mountain. It describes it well, too. My apologies to any Welsh speakers, by the way, as my translation is rather free, I believe.) Snowdon has a squat concrete building, which the train pulls up to, and which spews forth hordes of people, crowds that dilute the mountain to such a degree that despite it being huge, there is not enough to go around. Places on the trig point must be fought for, the view is hard to see through the wall to wall carpet of visitors. The management of this famous site is awful. We completed our task, but there was a slightly bitter taste to its conclusion.

As well as eccentric teachers, I had some good friends, most of which have now moved on, and with whom I have no contact. My best mate, though, a chap called James, I still see from time to time. He, too, arrived late at Packwood, though I don't recall why. He is a slightly puddled bloke, musical, and keen on many of the same academic subjects as I am. Through one of those quirks of fate, I was in his dormitory and/or his form for nearly my whole time at Packwood. We got on very well, and I remember a number of memorable occasions when he came to stay with me in the holidays, or I with him. One Easter, I remember very well, he invited me to come on a canal barge holiday for a week with him and family. We went up the Llangollen canal, into Wales, which was wonderful, as it is an exceptionally beautiful piece of countryside, and also has the fantastic Pont-y-cyllic aqueduct. This has got to been seen to be believed. It is a couple of hundred feet high, and half a mile long, and is built on Victorian brick arches. (I think there are twenty-two, but I can't remember offhand, so don't quote me on it) On top of this is the channel of the aqueduct, which is simply a steel trough, of about an inch thick. The practical upshot of this is that as you cross, there is the towpath on the one side, with a very flimsy railing, and nothing on the other side but empty space and a small, steel, edge. Oh, and a two hundred foot drop. I was ten, maybe eleven at the time, and thought that this was fantastically cool. James's mum, Davina, was having kittens about us all the way across, and his dad, Adrian, was firmly clenched to the tiller, and looking in a very straight line ahead. We were sitting on the front of the boat, oohing and aahhing at the drop.

I had three years at Packwood, and enjoyed them, by and large. The final year was gearing up for the most difficult exams in existence, the scholarships.

The English Public School system of Common Entrance and Scholarships is simple enough. Unless you are like me, and find a scholarship route, people in this country have two basic options for education. To pay, or not to pay. This is indeed the question. If you don't, you go to a state school, some of which are very good indeed, like the vast majority of people. If you do, first you go to a prep school, then you do one of two things. You take common entrance, which is a common set of papers for entrance to public school at 13, or you sit a scholarship. The Scholarships are the most fiendishly difficult exams ever. They are designed to sift out the best, and to prove to be impossible to everybody sooner or later.

The logic goes like this. If you set an exam that everyone can pass, then you have gained no information, except that the minimum standard is higher than the standard of your exam. If you set an exam that spreads people evenly across the range, then some people will be very good, some will be very poor, and most will be in the middle. You will get some, however, who are so good, or so bad, that they fall outside the range of measurement of your test, i.e. they get 0 or 100 percent.

The scholarships are directed at these top few percent. If you arrange the exam so everyone fails somewhere, then you have a measure of how good all the best people are. There will be a great many people who could get a reasonable mark on a common entrance paper, but very few who can get anywhere near a good grade on a scholarship paper.

Of course in GCSE and A level, the aim is different, and you are judging people against a standard and you want an even

24

spread of results around the standard required. Its a pity the examining boards seem to screw this simple concept up so regularly.

I loved the scholarship. It was hard, but fun, too. The questions were of that specially taxing sort that were hard enough to be really interesting, but not totally intractable. They were the kind of questions that you could really have a go at, and it didn't matter terribly if you didn't get the whole answer out as you weren't necessarily expected to.

The best paper was the General Paper. Years later, I found out that my housemaster Dr Gailey had set this fiendish paper, and we had a good laugh about the young me sweating over it.

The format of the paper was that of about fifteen essay titles, and 90 minutes to write answers to two of them, a free choice. I am tempted to go and find the actual paper, and include it verbatim here, but I think a few examples of the sorts of things that were asked should be sufficient to terrify anyone.

Remember these questions were asked of thirteen year old's. (Or in my case, 12 and 7/8 ths)

The questions I chose to answer, preferring them to others, were these two:

1: Has sport replaced religion as the opiate of the people?

2: George Bernard Shaw said that 'Those that can, do; Those that can't, teach.' Does this account for the failure of our education system?

Others I remember include such niceties as 'Manners maketh man. Discuss.' and 'Can man survive without music?'. Some among you may feel that to ask twelve and thirteen year old's to answer these kind of really quite sophisticated questions is ludicrous, as they cannot possibly make any head way. Well,

25

they can, and do. At the level that some of the people who take this exam work, they can get a start, and you can tell a lot about the candidate simply from which questions he answers. If he understands them sufficiently to pick the easier ones, then that has told you something.

I forget exactly what my argument about sport was, but I think I said something like that I did think that sport was the new religion, and cited things like the regular attendance to football matches on a Saturday afternoon rather than church on a Sunday, and drew similar comparisons with other aspects of the idea. I do remember how my argument about education goes, in fact it went something like this...

'Those that can, do, those that can't, teach.' No, no, no, you've got it all wrong. 'Those that can teach, teach. Those that can't, decide education policy and become the school inspectors.'

I spent a bit longer than that saying it, like about a side and a half of A4, but, roughly, that was what I said.

I got a B++ for that paper.

Chapter 3 – The Start at Eton

I didn't get the kings scholarship. I wasn't good enough. The eventual scholars were all people who were very good at everything, and, anyway, I didn't offer Geography, Greek or History as scholarship subjects, so I wasn't likely to be able to compete with the kind of people who could walk into every exam available with very few worries. The Kings Scholars go into College, but my earlier scholarship covered me anyway, and I was duly allocated to a house.

Eton is a very ancient school. It was founded in 1440 by Henry VI for the education of seventy poor scholars that Henry wanted educating in order that he had a loyal set of potential civil servants. As time went by, it evolved into a much bigger school. 'Collegers' who were the Kings Scholars (KS's) were provided for by the Foundation. 'Oppidans' who were all other boys who stayed in boarding houses in the town, and turned up for the same lessons. There were only two classes to start with, the Upper and the Lower Divisions, and only two masters, the Head Master, and the Lower Master. By all accounts, the times were wild. Naturally, it is a bit more organised now, and there is a system of Houses, whose historical roots are in the original boarding houses that used to put up the Oppidans during term. College still has seventy scholars, and the rest of the school is now divided into twenty four other houses of about fifty boys each.

I was bothered about being a 'mere' Oppidan at the time, but shortly afterwards decided that Manor House, which is where I ended up, was much better, anyway, as the people were a lot more normal. Scholars were weird. They generally fell into two sorts, the clever sort, who never did any work at all, and still came top, and the not quite so clever sort, who simply had no life, since they spent most of it working.

My house was kind of in the middle of the school. Actually, most people claim that their house is in the middle, but then the middle of Eton is not clearly defined. The school is just down the road from Windsor castle, and to the south of Slough. It is not a campus site, but organised more like a collegiate university, like, say, Oxford, with buildings spread around half the town. Its about half to three-quarters of a mile across.

My house was next to the library, which is a great big circular lead domed thing, and has been the subject of many many climbing attempts (and successes. Hehehe) It's not the biggest of houses, nor the best facilities, but it had the best people, and the best house character. All the houses have a character and culture peculiar to themselves, which is passed on from year to year.

Well, I arrived one sunny September day not knowing any of this. The new boys arrived in the morning of the Wednesday, and the rest of the school arrived back that evening. We obviously had to have the guided tour etc., and be told all those useful bits of information that are essential to life, like where the bathroom is. We also needed to sign in, in the big black book. All Etonians sign this as they arrive, and it is done with a certain amount of ceremony. I seem to remember my dad saying something encouraging at the time, like 'Well that's that then. You've done it now. Signed away the next five years of your life. No backing out now, you know.' Thanks Dad. Its good to know I can rely on you for a comforting word at a nervous moment.

Manor House was a bit of a maze - at least at first, as it is one of those organic houses, the sort that grew from the initial old building, and has been extended, and protracted, and added to and otherwise modified, and so on, until we arrive at the situation where there is five floors worth of windows on the outside, but only three floors on the inside at one point. Proper architecture.

All new boys start with the infamous new-boys tea party. This is a great social event and provides the new boys, the Housemaster, and the parents chance to get to know each other. And to sample genuine Eton cucumber sandwiches with the crusts cut off.

Mr Jaques was my housemaster. His full name was Nigel John Trefusis Jaques, which was excellent for chanting at football matches as it scans beautifully into a house football song. He's a wonderful chap, an unchanging figure, and he has always looked the same when ever I have seen him - tall and thin and giving a faint impression of having too many elbows. I have nothing but the highest regard for him. Anyway, the tea party was a success, largely due, I think, to the subtle efforts of Mr Jaques to introduce various families to one another in a way that he thought, quite correctly, they would get on with each other. At least, that is my opinion. I hope he did it deliberately, as I think he is the sort of person who could.

The members of my year in my house were quite a bunch of characters. There were nine of us, Me, Will, David, James, Richard, Marcus, Harry, Chris, and another Will.

Will and Dave were my best mates for much or the time we were there, though naturally we used to drive each other nuts on a relatively regular basis. They have totally different characters. Will is wild, untamed, nutty as the proverbial fruitcake, and very talented musically. He has the irritating ability to sit down with an instrument and figure out how to play it. He has the even more irritating habit of being able to sit down at a piano and just play, improvising as he goes along. He does not give himself enough credit for being able to do this. He is also a lot cleverer than he thinks, too. Dave on the other hand is very different. He is not as wildly extrovert as Will, and he loves gadgets. He likes mobile phones, and big hifi systems, and computers. OK, I like computers, but there is a difference. He just likes them to play with. I like plugging things together. He is also nuts about cars. He currently has a Fiat Punto upon which he bestows a great deal of love and attention. Mad.

The three of us, must have been a right combination to deal with. I take my hat off to Mr Jaques, and Dr Gailey after him, for not going quietly insane. Especially with 47 other highly eccentric boys in the house.

The others are a great bunch, a motley crew who despite a number of differences over a large part of our time at Eton, are basically good people to have known. At one time or other, as we passed through Eton, I have valued their company. Anyway, some of the things we got up to were legendary.

Eton has a language all to itself, that has developed over the centuries. One of the first things that happened was that picked up the various terms used by other people so that within a short period of time we knew what people were on about. I will, no doubt, lapse into using this, so here is a quick explanation.

Houses are known by their Housemasters initials, hence I was in NJTJ when I arrived, and once Dr Gailey had taken over the house, the name changed to ALHG.

30

A term is known as a half, as there only used to be two of them. They are the Michaelmas, the Lent, and the Summer Halves.

A year of boys is known as a block. Hence F Block is the first year, equivalent to the third year in most comprehensive schools, or even Year Nine in National Curriculum-ese. B block is the Upper Sixth. There is no A block, for complex historical reasons. There are a lot of things about Eton that involve complex historical reasons. Periods are called Schools. Thus you would have third school on a Wednesday. A class of pupils is called a Division, as in 'the people in my Chemistry division'.

Masters were called Beaks, which is convenient, since the term implies no gender, so you can equally well have a female beak as a male one, whereas a female master is a bit awkward, grammatically. A rare example where Eton leads the way in political correctness.

At a boarding school, we obviously did not have home work, but its equivalent was called EW's - extra work - this was given out to be done and handed in by a given date. It was done in our free time, and arranged as we saw fit. Just as long as it was in on time.

The first half in F Block consisted largely of learning the ropes, getting to know the school, which is quite big, and trying to work out what hit you. Fortunately, they were easy on the work load for a while, while you got your bearings, and provide useful things like a map of where the various school rooms are and how to find the various football pitches.

It also consisted of relaxing, realising were we not at prep school now, and that the rules were a lot less restrictive. Suddenly we had loads of free time that we had never had before, since at prep school they filled the time between getting up and going to bed with absolutely anything they could think of so as to keep us as occupied as possible so that we didn't hang about making mischief.

Naturally, then, we spent our new found free time getting up to all sorts of things. One particularly memorable event happened one quiet afternoon when we had nothing better to do. I don't remember whose they were, but someone's well-meaning mother had sent a punnet of kiwi fruit for their darling son, and of course he didn't like them. So they had sat in his cupboard for about three weeks, and had really started to go squashy, until some bright Herbert decided to start a fruit fight. So those rotten fruit were instantly rather desirable, and we had a huge fight up and down the length of corridor, until we ran out of fruit, and there wasn't enough left over that had not been ground into the carpet and walls to pick up and throw. It was messy, but unforgettable.

My Dame was not amused. An Eton Dame is sort of the equivalent of matron, at other boarding schools, but that does not begin to describe her job. Her responsibilities are legion. They involve everything not directly academic or sporting in the house. That is, she does accounts, doles out medicine, deals with deliveries, laundry, deals with food, and in short, runs all those things without which the house would not run. In our particular case, she is also the best Dame in Eton. Her name is Elizabeth Heathcote, and she is wonderful. She is the stuff that the empire was built on, the kind of go-getting lady who is not someone to cross. The sort of lady who would cheerfully set off up the Andes in full Victorian dress including button boots, where necessary. Terrifying in F block, and yet comforting, in a strange kind of way, and much loved by B Block.

One of my first lessons at Eton was English, with my old

32

friend the headmasters wife, Poppy Anderson. She remembered me, though I did not realise at the time, and she then said to me word to the effect of 'Hello there, do you not remember me? I am the GUIDE' At this point I wanted the ground to swallow me up. Nobody else in the room had a clue what we were on about, of course. Good job, really, or I would not have shown my face in school again.

We were expected to participate in, and/or support if we weren't playing, the house sport efforts. I was particularly useless at football. As for the field game, to which I was introduced to in my second half, that was a game that took a long time to love. It is a sport peculiar to Eton (some say its just peculiar). I did eventually learn the rules, at least sufficient to play in the bully (equivalent to scrum). The field game is very strange indeed. It evolved in much the same way as rugby did. Rugby was started at Rugby school, when someone picked up the ball and ran with it. Eton has a similar football variant, which is a quarter rugby and about three quarters soccer, but with more mud than either. It is universally hated by the lower school, (F and E block) however, once you have understood the way it works, and the fact you need to actually try to get any satisfaction, you fall into two groups in the rest of the school, those who love it, and those who hate it. To say that the rules are complex is an understatement. Some examples: The scrum equivalent is called the bully, which forms up lopsidedly, to give an advantage to one or the other side. The members of the bully are not allowed to hook the ball back, which is called furking. The team members are not allowed to pass the ball, unless within the bully, as it forms a loose mass of bodies and heads up the field. The closest equivalent to offside is called cornering or sneaking, dependent on the circumstances, where if the ball is kicked from behind you, up the field, you must retreat back as far as a member of the opposite team first, before

33

running up the field. This is sneaking. Cornering I never did fully understand, except it's to do with acting independently of the bully. Add a whole separate set of rules for the fly, which I never learnt, since I always played in the bully, and a scoring system which involves such niceties as Rouges and Rams, and you have a great game. I loved it, eventually, once I got to play in the slightly more senior games, where most people knew the rules, but to start with, it was my Tuesday afternoon Nemesis.

In the summer half, we were given a choice. We could be wet bobs, or dry bobs. That is, do cricket, or rowing. I had had enough of cricket at prep school, so opted for rowing. This was not the nice, gentle rowing you may be thinking of, mucking about on the river with Ratty, oh no. These were racing boats, designed to perform, and they were very narrow, very long, and very unstable. It is great sport, on the first afternoon of rowing each summer to watch the new boys fall in. The trick, with these boats, is to realise that the sculls act as outriggers, and stabilise the boat, and that if you keep them together and level, and spread out with the blades feathered, you can't fall in. However, its not that simple when you are out there on the water, and you really, really don't want to fall in, and you wobble as a big cruiser passes, and you start to correct it, and you overdo it, and suddenly the world is dark green, and very, very, cold. I never took to rowing. I mean, I could do it, and I did, but mainly I used it as an excuse not to play cricket, which always struck me as the most boring game ever. I didn't mind the rowing, I just got fed up doing of the same stretch of river over and over again. I got bored with the scenery. Actually, it's not bad. It just gets rather monotonous after a while.

It is during the summer term, that the Rowing fraternity get their big chance to show off. The Fourth Of June Holiday. This is held on the nearest Wednesday to the Fourth, which usually

34

means the end of May, and marks the start of half term. It is the closest to an open day that Eton gets, and everyone's parents come down, to socialise and see what's going on. There are numerous exhibitions on in various departments, and all the various sportsmen and team members get to show off their skills. The most ostentatious, though, are the rowers, who hold the Procession Of Boats.

The Procession Of Boats happens early in the afternoon, and draws a huge crowd. The members of the rowing team are all decked out in their best blazers and suits, and have straw boaters, on which they spend considerable time attaching huge numbers of flowers. Then, they take it in turn to row down past the crowds, and as they pass, they must ship their oars and stand up, then wave their hats to shake the flowers off into the water. Remember this is in a Racing Eight, an extremely long boat which is only perhaps two feet wide.

Each team in turn does this, and obviously the attraction of the event is to see if any of them fall in. There are dire punishments if they deliberately go over!

After this entertainment, everyone retires to the playing fields for a picnic.

You can tell a lot about people from their picnic. There are those, like us, who have a common-or-garden picnic. We have tuna and mayonnaise butties from a Tupperware box, we brew up a cuppa from a camp stove, and perch ourselves on a blanket or folding chair.

Then there are those who feel the need to throw a huge flashy affair. They turn up, in a gleaming waxed Mercedes, roll out the long oak tables, put up a marquee, pull out the cut glass crystal ware and the butler and other paraphernalia essential to their status. They eat caviar and champagne and pre packed salads with complicated dressings and, of course, the obligatory smoked salmon. Their territory is marked with flags, so that it cannot be missed by the roving socialites who flit from party to party all afternoon.

The strangest phenomenon are the really rich. The really rich people of this land are a funny breed. Often, they have no money. Oh, sure, their estate is worth millions, but that doesn't mean they have any money to hand, necessarily. They don't need it, secure in the knowledge that their ancestral wealth is not going anywhere. They turn up, usually in a muddy Rangerover or tired Volvo, find a quiet corner, and pull out a tatty tartan blanket. (Don't ask me why, but they are always tartan). They then have the requisite quails eggs, and champagne, but the stuff is religiously unpacked from an ancient and creaking hamper that granny bought. The reason the ancestral rich are rich, is that when they buy something, they buy it once, and the next five generations also get to use it. They are rich because they don't need to spend any money.

Out of the families that we have met and got to know via Eton, the ones we get on best with are those of a similar financial situation to our own, or those who have old money. I think the reason is that neither party need worry about money. We haven't got any, and they have so much, that we can just get on with being ourselves, and nobody needs any pretensions.

For the first twelve months at Eton, we were all being brought to the same academic standard. The problem with this was that those who had been through the scholarship like myself, and particularly the Kings scholars who had passed the scholarship, did no real work and learnt nothing new for a long time. When we finally hit new material, around about the start of the second year, it was a bit of a shock to get going again, as we had been simply ticking over since prep school.

Chapter 4 - The Runup to GCSE's

E block is the worst year at Eton. It is a year when you have no sympathy as you are no longer the smallest people around, as there are a whole load of new little F blockers to worry about, and you are not big enough to be trusted, and you get no privileges whatsoever, and on top of that you are loaded up with huge amounts of work, and the most number of subjects at any one time - I did Maths, English, Physics, Chemistry, Biology, French, Latin, History, Geography, Design, Divinity and P.E. This, along with a weekly tutorial with my Tutor at the time, John Claughton, filled 36 out of 35 available teaching periods a week. Mr Claughton is an amazing chap. I have a very high respect for him. He is a classicist, a very intelligent man. He also has a magnificent turn of phrase in his reports that he wrote about me. My parents used to look forward with great glee to his letters which came with my reports at the end of each term. These usually had them in hysterics. While he was my tutor, he got married, and had a son, and the change in him was marked. He mellowed. I have never seen a man melt so completely under the glow of his son. It was clear that the power of that baby to make him go gooey was a force to be reckoned with.

In the summer term, we also had GSCE's to take (early ones), and end of term exams, and lessons to deal with.

We took three GCSE's a year early, which were Maths,

French, and Latin. Everyone took these. Some, including myself also took the Maths Extension paper.

Due to the vagaries of the timetable, I tended to see a lot of certain people. One such figure, is a good friend of mine called Ed. I think that at the time, in all bar four of the weeks schools we were together, and due to our surnames both starting with 'R' we were for the most part seated together. Consequently, I got to know him really quite well. He is a bit of a one off. Most of my friends are, but Ed particularly is his own man. He is highly intelligent, even by the exacting standards of Eton and Cambridge, and cuts a singular figure. He is extremely tall and thin, almost gaunt in his appearance, with a shock of orange hair, and a large pair of glasses. During the time when I was ill, and stopping at the San, he stands as possibly the most frequent visitor. I have terrible trouble when he rings me or visits, as it is nearly impossible to finish a conversation with Ed, as he can, and does, talk easily and without apparent effort on any given subject with me. Every time I think the conversation is drawing to a close, he opens up another train of thought, and we switch tracks again to follow the new line to its conclusion. He is equally happy discussing the intricacies of back-stage theatre work, in which he spends a lot of time working as technical crew, or some esoteric subtleties of the latest in the world of computing. I gather he is an expert bingo caller, too, but I have never been privileged to witness this personally. I do not see him often enough these days.

One only has to mention GCSE's and there will be a great fracas about the National Curriculum, declining standards and the fact that O levels were much harder and the youth of today don't know they're born. Its an interesting debate. I think that the GCSE's could be better. Equally there were a lot of problems with O levels. And yes, in certain ways, some important, some not, GCSE's are in my opinion easier.

I was having this discussion with my Dad, and to settle the matter once and for all, we managed to get hold of an O level Maths paper and compared it directly with my GCSE ones, of which I had copies. The differences were interesting.

The O level was harder in some ways. The questions were framed differently, they required a much higher level of mathematical maturity, by which I mean the ability to see what the question was about and construct the required diagrams etc. from the description given, then to solve the whole question without further guidance. The GCSE approach was to have a multi part question to lead you through the process of solving the problem, and the diagram would be supplied. The difficulty of the actual maths involved however was comparable. It was simply the presentation and style of the paper that was different. The O level questions were also worked to use nice numbers, as there were no calculators at the time, only slide rules and log tables. The differences were stylistic. I assume that this is reflected across the range of exams. There is a problem here. On the one hand, making the questions more accessible helps greatly, and tends to spread the range of marks out, so that it becomes easier to grade people. On the other hand, being able to devise a method of solving a problem without too much guidance is a necessary skill for the real world. Being able to deal with jargon and the more exact terms of reference used in maths at a slightly higher level is a useful skill. Perhaps a combination of approaches is needed.

And while we are on the subject of maths, I want to say something on calculators. Calculators are the most abused maths tool ever. They are a godsend, a blessing, and are, and should be, used at GCSE level and up. They should not become a replacement for mental arithmetic, though, and they have.

I was in our local shopping centre the other week, and I saw in a shop, a calculator, marked up as 'Baby's first learn to count calculator'. This is a contradiction in terms. I was gob smacked. You can't teach people a sense of number with a calculator. You certainly shouldn't teach them to count with one in the first place. People should not be allowed to use calculators in school until they are able to manage without them.

The problem comes when the poor student hits the wrong button, and gets a nonsensical result. They just then blindly copy down the answer, and don't think. Thinking is the key. The essential thing to have, the most important, is a sense of how big numbers are, and why, for instance, it is wrong to multiply 100 by 100 and get 1000. To know that the square root of 9000 must be less than 100, since the square root of 10000 is 100. To be able to guesstimate, to work with orders of magnitude, and dimensions of results, so that if you tackle a problem and get an answer with a funny unit, then you've multiplied by the wrong thing. If you simply use a calculator all the time, you have no concept of the way number systems work, and you end up with far more trouble abstracting later on at, say, GCSE, and you never really get to understand such terrible things like equations.

If a calculator is used properly, it is OK. It is used as a tool to speed up calculation, to set the user free from having to do long division and or using tables for trig. But that is all. It should be an aid to arithmetic, not a replacement for it. In my class, when we covered factorisation of polynomial expressions in maths A level, (don't worry, I wont go into what the details are!) you use a method which is effectively long division. Half the people had to be taught long division first, then the factorisation. People are going to find maths less rewarding and harder at higher levels if their basic arithmetic is founded on a calculator, not on a fundamental understanding of the principles of arithmetic.

In E block, despite the timetable, I had a great deal of fun. It was during the summer term that me and my friend Will first discovered climbing.

It was a fine summers day and we were wandering about, and we came past the swimming pool. There was a fir tree by the door to this pool that lead directly up to the roof. I bet Will he wouldn't climb it, and he bet he would. Will being Will, he did. Then he disappeared, and reappeared about five minutes later at ground level, walking round the corner of the building towards me. I wanted to know what he had done, and he explained that there was another tree on the other side that you could climb down and so go from one side to the other.

Naturally, then, we both went on the next time across, and many subsequent times, and this opened our eyes to the possibilities of the school buildings. So we explored the backs and sides of buildings, and skulked in the shadows, and got very good at climbing, running, jumping, shinning up drain-pipes, over tiles, and generally not getting caught. We climbed most of the major school buildings, sooner or later. This included the Theatre, Drawing Schools, Allington schools, Caxton, Our own house, the Library, James schools, the School of Mechanics, Birley schools, and all the Gym complex, which was brilliant, as you could start in the street on Common Lane at one end, and get right across to the far side of the squash courts, covering the .22 rifle range, the Whitely Hall, the main squash courts, the indoor pool, the rest of the squash courts, and then down a convenient drainpipe at the other end. Over the next year or two we 'bagged' most of the remaining major school buildings, with only a few exceptions, notably Queens schools, School Hall, and the College buildings. We kept this up as something to do from that summer term in E block right through to C Block. For those who know Eton, I recommend the squash court roof for sunbathing.

I am not sure what would have happened if we had got caught. I got the distinct impression that while roof climbing would have had a very dim view taken of it, we would not have been in that much real trouble. The trouble would have come from getting caught. This is not a theory that I ever tested, but I got the general impression that with some of the school rules, the crime was breaking them, and with others, the crime was getting caught.

D block was wonderful after E. We finally got to choose our subjects, and, having passed GCSE French and Latin, I could drop them, and do only those subjects that I was interested in. Also, we had a number of free teaching periods a week (optimistically known as readers, as we were meant to spend them working. Fat chance.) for the first time, and these tended to be at really sensible times of the week, like last lesson on a Friday. This was a godsend. In D block, too, we were no longer considered part of the lower school, which meant beaks started to regard you as nearly human.

There was another big change in D block - my old House-master, Mr Jaques, gave up his house and handed over to Dr Gailey. Dr Gailey is a quiet Irishman, whose normally placid appearance hides a piercing intelligence which knows far more about what goes on in the house than a lot of people realise. He knows what to ignore and what not to, the sure sign of a razor blade brain hiding inside a reserved image.

To our eyes, he had a lot of strange ideas about running a house at first, but we soon got him into shape. The best thing about Manor house is its cheerfully unstoppable momentum. The house has a character which is at the same time tongue in cheek and serious, and it knows what to treat as which. There is a very highly developed sense of right and wrong, and where the line is. This was partially a legacy of Mr Jaques, who used to draw the fine line with a fine hand, and expected people to stick to it, without really checking. Woe betide you if you got caught, but you were trusted not to be stupid. He did not explicitly state what was allowed and what was not, but everyone knew whether a given action was above board or not. Dr Gailey, at first, tried to lay down every letter of the law, to make his position on where the line was clear. To some extent this was needed, and to some extent it was successful, but anything the house as a whole did not agree with was cheerfully ignored. Manor House just rolled on. Dr Gailey soon revised his approach, and took more things on trust, having discovered after a very short period of time that that got better results out of us. He rapidly got himself established in the house, not an easy thing to do, and the house then began to change more quickly. As time went on, it became ALHG, not NJTJ, the essential step. Most of the things that Dr Gailey did were for the better. A change of leader is always stressful, and the house successfully navigated it, largely due to the combined excellence of its housemasters. As time went by, and our year approached the top of the house, we began to appreciate Dr Gailey more and a mutual respect started to build. Myself, I had decided relatively quickly that I liked and respected the man.

I did AO Maths, English (Language and Literature), Physics, Chemistry, Biology, Design, and Geography. A fine timetable, as these were four schools a week each, apart from Maths and English, which left five readers during the week, which simply made life much more civilised.

43

Naturally, D block contained the bulk of my GCSE's, plus AO Maths, and the start of Maths A level. This too, was bearable, since teaching stopped at half term in the summer half, and we were free. The schools outdoor pool was open, and we used to spend a lot of free time out by it, sunbathing with some textbooks, running into the water every now and then to cool off.

The pool, by the way, is fantastic. Its the largest privately owned pool in Europe, and its perimeter is a quarter of a mile. Aeroplanes use it as a landmark for finding Heathrow. It also leaks badly, so it must be constantly topped up from the well dug for this purpose, which is fine, but it means that it never really warms up, and it is always a bit of a challenge to get in. I took the slow and sedate method, lowering inch by inch as the parts of me underwater numbed. Others took the 'jump straight in to get it over with' method, which is fine, but personally I'm not that brave. The pool has two huge diving boards which are great, as the top board is about twenty feet up. I used to regularly leap off, but the people who impressed me were the ones who could pull off one-and-a-half somersaults and other spectacular dives. I did try, but I hurt myself just from a lower board, as I had my hands wrong. I never really plucked up the courage to try again.

GCSE's came and went, and I duly got my results, which were excellent. I felt strangely dissatisfied, though, as they weren't a surprise. There was nothing in them to get excited about, as we had been so well prepared, and we knew the stuff we were meant to, and had followed the advice given, and had done enough practice papers to know exactly how good at the various papers we all were, that when the results finally came, there was no anticipation, no surprise, nothing to celebrate. My mum and dad didn't seem to understand for a long time what was up, why I was frustrated and upset, when I should have been overjoyed at a first class set of results. They told me later that they did understand, just they didn't know what to do about it. I know a lot of my friends felt the same about their results. I have a far greater respect for someone who gets ten A stars at a standard comprehensive, than for similar results from a top public school. While both are excellent, the differences in expectation and competition and culture means that it is far more of an achievement at the state school.

Also at this time, I had to chose a 'Specialist Tutor', for the duration of my sixth form. I wanted Mr Desborough. He is a design teacher, who works down in the School Of Mechanics, and is someone who I had already decided was better than the average teacher, and was not a bad human being, too. The process of choosing a tutor involves writing them a letter asking them if they would do the job. There is an official list, too, of those tutors who make themselves available. Mr D was not on it. I went to see him, in order to first persuade him to go onto the list, then to take me on as a pupil. Well, he agreed, eventually, and then we had to go through all the formal rigmarole as well, to satisfy the system. I have a great letter from him, saying that he would be glad to be my tutor, in response to my deadpan letter asking if he would be. Of course, we had arranged it all weeks previously.

For my A levels, I chose to do Double Maths, Physics, and Design. I also did AS level Psychology as an optional extra subject. This was not an easy decision, as it was a close call between doing Chemistry and doing Design. The problem was that at some Universities, Design is still not regarded as a 'proper' A level. I think that it is an excellent discipline, and teaches you a lot of things that are not taught elsewhere in the curriculum. These include such essential life skills as a structured problem solving method, proper time and project management, presentation skills, and a lot of work on methods of communicating your ideas effectively, as well as the more practical skills and lessons that result from actually physically making something. The scope within Design for excelling at your chosen facet of technology or another discipline such as silverwork or woodwork, and using personal knowledge and interests that are not directly from school experience is phenomenally large. You can bring a little of the real commercial, hard edged business and manufacturing world into the cloistered environment of a school, and demonstrate real practical uses of all the accumulated knowledge of your years of education. It forces you to really research, to work with the limitations of the real world, and not nice, neat, idealised problems from other subjects. Design is a hugely relevant discipline, and a working knowledge of design processes is a huge boon to students going out into the real world. Anyone who aspires to do something, make something, produce something, be it a service, a newspaper, or a fighter plane, benefits from learning to solve problems.

Needless to say, I chose to do Design, despite its image with university admittance tutors.

Mr Desborough turned out to be a great choice of tutor. In our first official meeting, at the start of C Block, (Lower Sixth) he took us out on his boat, for a quiet evening cruise up the river. Immensely civilised. Later that term, he organised a dinner party. No, not one for us to come to, but one that we had to write our own guest list for, and prepare and cook the meal, serve it up, and generally play the host for the assembled guests.

There were two of us in the tutorial group, a very nice chap called Ricky, and myself. Between us, we figured out that we would be cooking for eight, and we went shopping with Mrs

Desborough for the requisite stuff, and we seemed to manage to put on a three course meal. We had a melon fruit salad for starters, with lasagne and salad for main course, and apple pie for pudding. I had done a certain amount of cooking before, at home, as my mum is of the practical school of thought, and had imparted certain gems of wisdom to me on previous occasions, but Ricky had not done anything remotely near this scale before. We had a wonderful time. He did the starter, I did the pudding, and we both worked on the immense lasagne. I must say, Rick was a star cheese sauce producer, and my short crust pastry on the apple pie, by some miracle, came out perfectly.

It was a fine evenings entertainment.

Chapter 5 - My Illness

The first problems that I had, I noticed on exercise on the CCF weekend at school. The CCF, or Combined Cadet Corps, is the school military cadet group, and boys have the option of joining in the Lower Sixth. It is run by various real services personnel and a few members of staff who are ex-servicemen. I had deliberated long and hard about joining the CCF. I had to balance the opportunity of doing some very fun things, like abseiling out of helicopters and flying planes against a certain amount of drill and square-bashing. I was not at all sure of this.

James finally made my mind up. He virtually dared me to join, and said that he thought I wasn't up to it. After that, I obviously had to.

Square bashing was as boring as it was rumoured. Marching about in perfect time is a lot harder than you might think, and it is not a particularly engaging way to spend your Monday afternoon. On the other hand I enjoyed many of the other things that we did, including the first exercise, which consisted mostly of command tasks and teamwork exercises. We as a group got wildly lost during the night exercises, and as a result, our second year cadet, responsible for leading us from task to task, got in a huge amount of hot water. Never mind, I enjoyed it, even if he did not. Another particularly fine moment was a trip to RAF Odiham. We were driven out there, and shown all sorts of cool things such as a 'G' force training centrifuge, then flown back in a Chinook. This was my first flying experience. We were kitted out in full combat suits, due to the fact that you do not wear clothes containing artificial fibres in the air, as in the event of an accident, the resultant fire causes your dress trousers to stick to your skin. We thought this was very reassuring. Anyway, we were flown back to school in this chopper, and we landed on College field, next to a football match between two houses. We then proceeded to practice our heli-drop drill, as soon as the helicopter touched down, of sprinting out of the helicopter, and forming a defensive fan position on the ground, while the helicopter zoomed back up again. The whole landing took less than a minute. The football game just stopped. There we were, in full combat gear, fanned out on the field, having appeared, unscheduled, in under a minute. We were killing ourselves laughing for a long time afterwards, at the sight of all these footballers just standing there, looking at us in that faintly dazed way that only the totally gobsmacked can muster.

There were two parts to the CCF, the army section, and the RAF. I was part of the RAF, who were obviously far superior to the army, and on the particular exercise in question, we were chosen to be the Enemy. The Army were the good guys. There is nothing like a bit of inter-services competition to get people enthusiastic. Seriously, the split was skilfully used to fire people up, and get people to really try, lest the other groups were proven to be better.

The exercise started off well. We were airlifted in Chinook helicopters to a snowbound field somewhere in the vicinity of Aldershot, complete with full pack and rifle, and told to make our way to point X, which was a line of Pylons that we as the Enemy had to defend. We spent most of the day jumping through hoops, and occasionally we would be imparted a piece

49

of intelligence, and told to march here, or ambush a party of the other team there, etc. We had a lovely time playing soldiers, anyway.

When we finally made it to the pylons, we set up a camp, complete with perimeter string and camouflage and so on, and settled in for the night. My leg had been hurting that day, but I thought it was a pull or something, and ignored it. We spent a fun time digging out our shelters, and so on, and settled in for the night, suitably equipped with sentries. During the night, we went out on a number of raids to local camps, and burst on various camps etc. and generally caused havoc. Obviously we were also raided and this was again cause for much excitement and running around.

My leg was giving me problems all night, and I was having trouble. I stayed at camp to guard for several of the raids, since I was having trouble running about.

In the middle of the night, the instructors came and kindly dropped thunderflashes on our bivouac's which woke us up rather sharpish. We scrambled for our weapons and repulsed the raiders, but I was slowing up by this stage and was really suffering with my leg. Come the next morning, I had to sit out of a number of the activities, since I could not run around much, and the exercise in question involved legging it away from the pylons to regroup. I walked it.

On return from the camp, I crashed out in bed for the rest of the Sunday.

On Monday morning, I went down to the Doctors, to see what he thought. He thought I'd pulled or twisted something, or maybe torn a ligament or cartilage or something. We had an X-ray done.

Later that week, I went back to the Docs for the results, and was told that there was nothing unusual on the X-ray, so it must be a soft tissue injury, and it would get better over the Easter Holidays (which were coming up). Take it easy, I was told, and it will get better in a few weeks. Hmmm.

I went home for the Easter holidays. I had a great time, as I arranged a stay with Eddie, a friend of mine at the time who lived in the Lake district. Conveniently, he had a car and could drive it, so he picked me up from Stoke as he passed going North, and we went to his house in Cumbria. We had a fine time, as we had planned, and did a walk over Hellvellen, and Striding Edge. This was great, but my leg was suffering by the time we got back. I assumed it was because I had overdone it. My leg was bad that week, but bearable, and I just got on with enjoying my self. We decided to visit Dave, who lives in Scotland, about thirty miles South of Edinburgh. His parents' farm is nice, and we had a trip up his hill on the back of a quad. I say a hill, it was quite big, and we sat on the trig point on top, and Dave pointed out the edges of their land.

Dave came with us, and we went on to Harrogate, to see yet another friend, Robin. My leg was bugging me by this stage, and I was in pain. I was worried about it. We had a pleasant evening, enjoying ourselves, watching daft videos, and so on, then departed, and Dave went home, and Eddie drove me south to home.

My leg was causing me further problems, now, and I wasn't sleeping well. I noticed a lump which had come up.

Eventually, we went to Accident and Emergency at the local Hospital, North Staffs, and they thought it was a soft tissue injury. The standard response was some pain killers, and a tubigrib bandage, and 'It will get better over the next few weeks'

51

It didn't happen that way.

The first day back in the summer term, my leg was very bad during chapel that morning, and so, after chapel, and during the head masters start of term speech, which I wasn't terribly bothered about, I went down to the school doctors again.

We arranged an X ray. He took a blood test, and there was a cock-up, and he had to do it again in the other arm, since the tube he used for the blood was faulty, and the blood went everywhere. Having had this happen, I got up and went out, feeling rather faint. The Sister, Linda, asked if I was OK, and discovering that I wasn't, told me to lie down, on the carpet, in the middle of the waiting room. Sue, the new staff nurse that term, came out from another door way. This was the first time I met her, lying horizontal on the carpet in the San at school.

I haven't mentioned Linda, or the San at all, really, so far, so its about time I did. Linda is the sister at the Sanatorium at Eton. The San is the school's medical building. It is an amazing piece of restorative architecture. It used to be a church, and it had fallen into disrepair. The school had bought the shell, and contracted out to an excellent architect to turn it into a useful building again. In the front, on the first floor, there remains a small chapel, which is used regularly as the local parish church separately from the school. There are also flats for the permanent staff and some of the masters from the school. Under that, there is the Doctors surgery for the vicinity. In the rear half of the building there is the San. This is the boys doctors surgery, which two of the GP's cover, and the rooms for boys off school due to being ill with whatever. Linda is the sister, with, at the time, two staff nurses, Sue, and Sally. (In the due course of time, Sally left for pastures new, and Angela came in her place. This was the state of affairs up until very recently. Now both Sue and Angela have left, and two new staff nurses have arrived. I had the strange experience last month of ringing the San and having someone answer who didn't know me!)

Linda is a great constant, a close friend who is very supportive, amusing and uplifting when I am miserable. Throughout my illness she has sent me postcards and other cards to let me know that she was there and was thinking of me. I don't know whether I ever told her, but just that simple gesture, notwithstanding everything else she did, did a great deal for me. Being able to come down the stairs in the morning and find yet another daft postcard from Linda waiting on the door mat gave me strength to get out of bed and find out if there was one.

Sue is another. She is a fellow Pratchett fan, and we both used to drive Linda nuts by quoting him at her. She is an exceedingly sharp lady, someone who behind the mild mannered bespectacled visage hosts a brain like a meat slicer. She has that genuinely pervasive wit that knows just how and when to say what to lighten the mood. I have a very high regard for her and consider her a close friend. Ringing her always cheers me up. There are a number of very fine books by Terry Pratchett, and Sue, Linda, and Angela, appear many times as an amalgam of various characters. I reckon Sue is a mixture of Nanny Ogg and Granny Weatherwax, with a bit of Susan, Deaths granddaughter, thrown in.

Well, I had the X ray, and this time, a mere six weeks after the first one, something showed on it. There was a great sense of Doctors running round in circles waving their hands in the air, and getting rather excited. I saw knee specialist in Windsor, who said that this was not his speciality, it was either a bacterial infection, or a growth. He referred me to Mr Cannon. Miss Heathcote ferried me down to a hospital in Harrow, where I had a biopsy.

We didn't get the results for a while. When we did, my parents, who had been quietly panicking at the time, but whom had hidden it very well from me at the time, travelled with me down to the hospital. Mr Cannon confirmed the diagnosis of Osteosarcoma. My parents asked me if I wanted to come home, and I said, No.

I don't know how my parents felt at this stage, but I didn't really understand. It took a long time for it to sink in that this was Cancer. It was described to me as a tumour, or a growth, or whatever, but mentally I did not connect what was happening to me with Cancer.

I wanted to lead as normal an existence as I could for the next few months, and normal by this stage meant stopping at school. Mentally, and whoever said people were logical, coming home was admitting that this was serious, and I did not want to believe that. I wanted to lead a normal life, and normal, once you have been to boarding school for a few years, is away from home. Home is where you go for holidays, or if you are really ill. I wasn't really ill, therefore why should I go home? My mum and dad presumably desperately wanted me home, but to their credit, they let me stop at school. They hid all the fear, the worry and the blind panic from me. I was still wildly confused, and didn't really connect.

I was referred to Professor Souhami, at the Middlesex hospital. This is the first time that I came on to the adolescent ward.

We went to this hospital as there were only two centres for the treatment of teenagers specifically with cancer in the country, and this one was closer to school. I still hadn't realised that this was a serious problem, and that it was potentially life threatening. I assumed that, yes, it would take six months out, but that it would be fixed.

In order to do this, we set me up to stay at school and a great deal of my things were transferred to a room at the San. The room was really superb. There are wonderful stone arches for the windows (it was, after all, a church) and these have an amazingly peaceful effect. The view was of South Meadow, a large playing field, across which sunbathers and returning rowers were liberally strewn during the summer. I was able to do a certain amount of work, and a lot of play, and a great deal of reading and listening to Music. Music and food were the two favourite topics of conversation between me and the staff.

Naturally, I had my bad days, my 'Black Wednesdays' and some 'Dark grey Fridays', too. The nurses were massively supportive at these times, and despite my best efforts to emulate Marvin, the Paranoid Android from The Hitch Hikers Guide, they did not let me get too fed up and took the mickey so effectively I ended up laughing at myself.

My first impressions of the ward were that it was small, and that there was a lot of stuff, well, just all over. The consultant, Prof Souhami, explained the situation and that the growth was malignant, that is it send out bits of itself which can then lead to secondary growths. This meant that I had to have chemo, a systemic treatment, that treated all of me, not just the main site. This was my first admission and it was explained to me that it would be a bit longer than the others, as they had to do some tests. OK, I thought. That's clear enough. Well, the Middlesex's definition of a few tests, and my definition, are two different things. I was in for ten days that first time, with my mum stopping, and only the last three or four were chemo. A whole battery of tests to check everything and more needles than you could shake a stick at were thrown at me that week. I had at least eleven holes in veins, and rapidly ran out of clear ones to use. I then had a minor operation to have a Hickman Line inserted. This is a brilliant invention to save having to use needles and other sharp things with long term patients. It is basically a tube which is inserted into a large vein, and brought out through ones tummy. This allows you to directly inject, take blood, and give infusions without having to break the skin again. It stays in for as long as necessary.

A specifically adolescent ward was a godsend. There is a problem in this country. Most people in hospital are very young, or very old. There are few in between. As a result, most hospitals have a paediatric ward for the young, and the rest are mostly full of older people, middle aged upwards. There is therefore a problem for those people who are too old for a paediatric ward, and yet get extremely bored with the company of fifty, sixty, seventy year old people. There is a need for facilities for people whole are between about thirteen and twenty-one. These eight years are a problem, and if there is a chance of finding people of your age group to natter with, hospital can be a whole lot better.

The ward at the Middlesex is like that, in fact it goes one better, as it is specifically for cancer patients. Had I been treated at home, I would most likely never have seen anyone with my condition, and it would be rare to see people of my age. I have been on the ward in London with four people of ages within a couple of years either side of me, with the same condition, on the same treatment, and with the same problems, hopes, and desires. That in itself is something to treasure. The support of people who are in the same boat is invaluable.

The plan was explained to us. The treatment was as follows: Six lots of chemo, the drugs used were Cysplatin and Doxorubicin, at three week intervals, with surgery to remove the tumour and replace my knee joint and tibia with a titanium

56

prosthesis instead. Its not much, if you say it quickly. It didn't really sink in. Nor did the fact that, really, it is impossible to stick neatly to the plan, and the timetable just doesn't work. The problem is that the reactions and results of the treatment are very difficult to predict exactly, and things must be taken as they go. Anyway, within a few days, the first chemo was connected up, and the first bag of drug was started. It was every bit as bad as it was meant to be. I was very sick indeed, even by the standards of the nurses on the ward, and threw up everywhere, in copious amounts, for about a week afterwards.

My mum was always there, to help, and make my life easier. The nurses threatened her with a uniform, on more than one occasion. What it was like for my dad, who stopped at home to look after my brother and sisters, I don't know. I don't know how he managed.

I have no idea what to say about my parents. As I have been writing this, I have skimped from writing about them, as I didn't know what to say, where to begin to talk about people who spent most of the year travelling up and down the M40 to see me, and juggle life at home with my three siblings with life in hospital with me. I was in hospital one week out of three with that first lot of chemo, and my mum stayed all the time with me. She used to travel up and down and up and down, and my dad used to drive up and down, and up and down, and they saw me nearly every weekend, and stayed when I had a dodgy patch and simply became part of the constant surroundings, always there for me, and always ready to help. If I don't mention them all the way through this, it is not that they weren't going through it all with me, its because they were always there, and it would be like describing the floor I stood on, and the ceiling that kept me dry.

I was told that the second chemo is rarely as bad as the first.

It was. It was worse. And I started to lose my hair. It's very strange to be able to literally tear your hair out by the fistful, but also satisfying, in a warped kind of way. The hair was falling out so quickly, now, that I just decided to shave it all off. So we cut it to a Mohican, first. I have some brilliant photos somewhere, of The Day The Hair Came Off. In stages. The best is me with a fine Mohican, a bald head other wise. Well, I had to take the opportunity, it's not everyday your mother will let you do something like that! It was done by Sue, and photographed by my mum. Sue is ace. Her job title is Activities Co-ordinator, which does not even begin to describe the range of things that she does. She has the unenviable task of attempting to keep the wards patients occupied and alert, and happy, and not utterly fed up 'cos they're feeling grotty, they are very ill, and there's three thousand things they'd rather do than sit up and be cheerful, and play Monopoly. I don't know anyone who is better at getting on with people. The ward is a centre of excellence, and as a result, draws not just NHS patients from this country, but private ones from all over. There have been occasions were I am the only native English speaking patient on the ward. We have had Arabic, Punjabi, Greek, and various others, and it must be so much harder for them, not necessarily speaking English. Sue just gets on with them all. I have the very highest respect for her.

It is amazing, though, what can be achieved with sign language. I remember an occasion, I don't remember exactly when, when a little girl (I say little, she was twelve) arrived in great pain, after a fourteen hour journey from Qatar. Neither her nor her mother spoke a word of English, and my mother spent the rest of that evening calming her mother down and extracting the story by dint of improvised sign language. When that ran out, she resorted to just giving her a hug. Sitah, the girl, was in a bad state, in a lot of pain, and spent most of the night

58

wailing. She was around a lot while I was in. She got much better as time went on, and they both could speak conversational English by the time they left for home.

I was now completely bald, and I suddenly discovered how useful hats are. I am told that thirty percent of body heat is lost through the head, and if you are bald, it must be far more than that. Whatever the facts and figures are, I discovered that hats were essential if I was to go out, as my head got very cold, very fast.

So it was that I started to build my hat collection. I still buy them, now, even though I have hair, and at the last count I have several dozen. They are in all shapes, sizes, colours, styles, and every one of them has a story. At time goes on, they get progressively wilder, too.

Among my favourites are my plain old green woolly hat, my mini ethnic embroidered skull cap thing, my giant purple top hat, and my Hat With Bells On. This last is a top hat variant, in yellow, violet, and turquoise velvet. It has six spikes on top, and attached to each is a small brass bell. It has been known to turn a few heads when I wear it in public. Unless I wear it in London, when of course, such things are as nothing compared to the haircuts that can be seen, and no-one bats an eyelid at my effort to get noticed. Anyway, a hobby that grew from an essential practical need grew into something far more interesting. If a few more people wore a silly hat occasionally, it would make the world a happier place. It brings a smile into other peoples day. If you can make just one persons day by giving them something to laugh about, then you've done them a very small service that costs you nothing.

I was very ill again, starting from half way through the infusion, and lasting a week. When I finally felt OK to eat, I got a sore mouth, with ulcers and so on. I was losing weight rapidly. When I started this game, I had been fourteen and a bit stone. I got down to ten, at my lowest. Then I got neutropoenic, again, and had to really careful of bugs and so on. That was not so bad, really, at this stage, but it was hard work. On the other hand, one advantage of the chemo was that the pain that I had been getting from my leg now ceased completely, which as you can imagine was very welcome.

I had been going to have the operation after my second chemo. However, there was an administrative cock-up, and due to this, it was postponed until after the third chemo. I should have been called to an appointment earlier to have some measurement films done, but this wasn't done, and as a result, they had not made my prosthesis.

Another great character on the ward was Margaret. She is the hospital teacher, and her job is to persuade all those in school to get on with a bit of work. It was she who organised for me to take certain modules of my Maths A level on the ward. Usefully, I managed to do this, and was able to complete it before I left school the following summer. I am great friends with Margaret, like Sue, and all of the other staff, too numerous to describe all of them in detail. The wash of names boiling in my memory is large, and a number of them have moved on. In fact, I have been on the ward longer than most of the nurses now, as there are only a few of the original crew left. There are many among them I consider close friends.

The third chemo was much better, and I was not as sick. I developed a fixation for Lucozade, and drank lots of it during that week. I have never been able to touch it since. The chemo used to do really strange things to my tastes, for instance I went nuts on Marmite, and Lucozade. I have always been keen on chilli con carne, but now I craved it. I went right off sandwiches. I went right off bread, in fact, any thing like that, cakes biscuits, sweets, and so on. I got back to eating a lot faster after this cycle, though.

Sooner rather than later, the end of term came, and I went home.

Chapter 6 - The Operation

It was my seventeenth birthday early in July, and I had a while off at home before I was admitted to the Royal National Orthopaedic Hospital, onto Colonel Wood ward, which is the adolescent ward there, on, I think, the 27th July, 1995.

If you imagine the classic ward, a long straight room with beds down either side. It is a big ward, with a lot of beds, and the image of the archetypal Florence Nightingale ward is only spoilt by the profusion of items for the amusement of teenagers, a snooker table, a collection of computer game consoles, and so on and so forth.

So it was when I arrived that Friday night, was given the ritual examination by a doctor on the ward, and told that the ward round would be along in a bit and that Mr Cannon, the surgeon, would see us then. Well, he was cheery. He told me that I had a one in twenty chance of losing my leg. This, as you can imagine, went down well with me. It was explained, that though the scan was apparently OK, if, when he opened it up, found that it was complicated, and he would not be able to cut it out with sufficient clearance to ensure that he got it all, then they would simply amputate. I had a bit of a sleepless night. The operation was on Monday. I had a lovely time, I woke up, was not allowed any breakfast, was put to sleep (which was cool, actually) and woke up five hours later in feeling like a lorry had run over me. I woke up in the Intensive Therapy Unit

(ITU). The first thing I did was to count my toes. Once I had safely passed five, I was happy. I dozed off again. I woke up, I was very groggy. I had loads of connections. I counted them - I had seven canulas, including one arterial link, an epidural for pain control (which I was very glad of), an catheter (which was put in while I was conscious - but fortunately, only just conscious), and a drain from the wound site. I was festooned with bleeping equipment and machines that went 'bing' every now and then. Fortunately I was enough out of it not to care.

After 48 hours, I went back to the ward, and I had my epidural out, and most of the others things out, and was given a PCA - a patient controlled analgesic. This was ace - it amounted to a giant syringe of morphine that I could press a button to inject some. There was a complicated machine to make sure I had the right doses for the amount of time and so on, but basically, it let me control pain easily. They are a fantastic invention.

I wasn't allowed to sit about and moan much, though. Within a very short space of time, the physiotherapists were on me. I had to start moving the leg and bending it as far as possible as fast as possible, and they weren't kidding. Within four days of the op, they had persuaded me to stand. Within a week, they were taking me off the ward as far as the physiotherapy department, as opposed to coming to me on the ward, and were persuading me to walk from the wheelchair to the couch and back again, and various exercises and things, and so on. The nickname on the ward was Physioterrorist, and this about summed it up.

I was told that I could not use my quadriceps muscle for the first six weeks, as this had to have time to heal itself. As a result, when ever I was weight bearing, I had my leg strapped in a splint, so that the knee could not bend. I also had foot drop.

63

This was a problem due to the surgery. My nerves to my foot were a bit damaged, and the foot was no longer responding properly, and the ankle joint would no longer lift the foot up. This I was told, could be permanent, and certainly would take a long time to heal. If it wasn't better in eighteen months, it wasn't going to be. Oh, right, I thought. Another little detail to this surgery lark that they neglected to tell me about. I therefore needed a further splint to ensure that the foot stayed up, and I didn't trip over it! I was told I needed to do lots of physio, and that the more I did, the better the leg would be. I was put on a CPM machine for long periods of time - this stands for Continuous Passive Movement, and it basically repeatedly bends and straightens the leg to a given angle and back again. This was fine, but people kept turning the control knob up a notch so that it went up another degree.

Despite all this, I enjoyed those days, as I felt I was getting somewhere. I had a number of visits from friends from school, both the staff and the boys, and there was a great deal going on on the ward to keep me occupied. I had a visit from Miss Heathcote. She brought up a huge basket of fruit. We still have the basket now, at home, and we still keep our fruit in it. My mum was stopping, and kept me on the straight and narrow and doing my exercises. My dad and siblings came to visit, too, but the day that they came, there was a huge crowd of people and so many on the ward that it was difficult, especially with the noise level. I dread to think how many thousand miles my dad drove that summer.

There were some real characters on the ward, too. One was Dominic. He was the patient in the bed next to me, and he had had scoliosis. The treatment for this condition, which causes extreme curvature of the spine, is to open up the patient's back, and effectively tie a bar to the spine to hold it straight. This, of course, has various knock on effects, and the patient must stay on his back, flat, for a long period of time. Whilst I was there, Dominic was allowed to sit up for the first time in I think it was six weeks. He went nuts at being able to see more than just his immediate surroundings, and turned to face me, (obviously we had been talking for a number of days, without really seeing one another, and said words to the effect of, 'Gosh, so that's what you look like'.

Another one was Zak, a rastafarian lad from London, whose language was a bit strong for some of the staff, and was famously heard to yell at a poor nurse "f*** off, leave me alone, I'm trying to read my f***ing Bible". Here however, is a good example of a very important lesson that life has taught to me. That is that people are a product of their background. They need to be placed in a context, just as much as a quote does. If you quote a piece of work out of context, you can work it so the quote means whatever you want, whatever you decide. It is the same to a large extent with people. Each human being on this planet of ours is unique, and needs to appreciated in their natural environment. I have seen a great many people in my life so far, from all walks of life. Before judging them, or forming opinions, you must take the time to try to discover the context from whence they originate. You need to know people intimately, before you can judge, and you must do it on an individual basis. Prejudice is easy. To know a person completely is impossible, so any judgement that you make is at best an approximation. To judge a person's behaviour, you must use their yardstick, their set of values and attitudes, and their viewpoint. If you do this, then all of a sudden, most people in the world behave far more reasonably.

Someone else I knew in hospital, actually it was in the

Middlesex, we'll call her Becky. She was a 21 year old single mother of two. She developed Cancer, and has spent all her time since trying to juggle life at home with her treatment. She lives a long way from the hospital. Her morals are the most impeccable of anyone I know. She wears a ring, that in her eyes, is just as binding as a marriage certificate, and the only reason she does not live with her partner is that it is not financially viable for them. She thinks the world of her children. She has a very highly developed sense of right and wrong. She knows where she stands on what, where her line is, and that's a lot more than a lot of people I can think of can do. There are a lot of prejudiced people who would look down on her who should take a deep look at their own standards first. She earned my deepest respect as someone who could continue a fight against even more ridiculous odds than many others on the ward.

Judge people by their yardstick, not yours. You end up liking more people.

My named nurse was a wonderful Irish lady called Donna. She was brilliant, and we had a great time one afternoon taking it in turns to remove the staples from my scar. My scar was ace. It is eighteen and three quarters inches long, and had 56 staples holding it. I learnt that with major wound sites like mine, they did not use stitches, and now used what was effectively a staple gun to hold the skin together. We used what was to all intents and purposes a standard staple remover, too. It was a bit strange, in a disconnected kind of way, to pull these pieces of metal out. I still have them, somewhere, in a little pot. Other wonderful members of staff included Alice, an extremely nice nurse. I was sick after the anaesthetic, as people often are. Only it was just after having drunk a cup of hot marmite, (Made by dissolving marmite in boiling water. Very nice with toast!) and

I threw up it all over the bed, and right down the front of her uniform as she dashed to get me a bowl. I think she forgave me, but she did say later that week, that she used to like marmite on toast, but now she doesn't know if she can face it. Janice, another staff nurse, was also a qualified aromatherapist, and used to come around and 'do' everyone who couldn't sleep due to whatever reason late at night. I had a foot massage every night for a week, as I was not sleeping well, and it was the best cure for insomnia I have ever found. She really did make a lot of people's lives a lot easier.

I went home after two weeks, strapped up, and on crutches, and trying to cope with getting about. One of the things that has never ceased to amaze me was the way that I got over the operation so quickly. Getting up and down stairs was a bit interesting, but I managed, and with the regular and religious application of my physio routine, my leg reached a steady state of being able to bend to about ninety degrees.

I was stuck with the knee splint for six weeks, and I had really had enough, and I wanted rid of it. Eventually, I was allowed to take it off, and just walk with the ankle splint. By the time I took it off, I could walk with only one crutch and the two splints, but I had to go back to two crutches and the single ankle splint. With the knee splint off, my physio stepped up a gear, and I was asked to try to get my thigh muscles working properly.

Well, I went back to the Middlesex for chemo four. This did not go well. I had been feeling grotty for a bit beforehand, anyway, and when they started the infusion, I developed sudden pyrexia, that is, a whopping temperature, and we were forced to remove the Hickman line and calm me down and give me loads of antibiotics and things through my arm and a vein. This of course meant needles - ow - and I then had the chemo through a canula in my arm, too. This would have been OK, but they couldn't put my Hickman back in till the next cycle, and I was really grotty with this one, and had all sorts of problems with my blood and so on, and required several transfusions as a result at home. These of course went in through my arm too. And the subsequent blood tests were done through my arm. I was ready to have my nice safe Hickman back, soon, please.

Due to all these shenanegins, I had to postpone my fifth chemo for a week. This was at least relatively uneventful, except that I had another Hickman in. This was a relief, but the problem with Hickman's is that ones shoulder is mega-sore for many days after it is put in. Also, with this cycle, they gave me some blood with it, to try to boost me up and tide me over the low patch, which was getting longer.

It was when my dad came down with my siblings to visit during this treatment, that my sister Kerry met Pork Pie, the ward pet. Pork Pie is a small brown hamster, and I think he has an amazingly apt name. We had to hang about for a while, I forget why now, and to keep Kirsty and Kerry happy, Sue asked them if they wanted to clean out the hamster cage. They said yes, and so they did. All was progressing famously, until there was a scream, and we turned round to see Kerry yelling, and Pork Pie hanging off her finger, his teeth sunk deeply into the flesh. All was pandemonium for a few seconds, until David, a staff nurse, separated Pork Pie and Kerry, Sue put him back into his cage, and my mum shipped Kerry round to Accident and Emergency, which was in a different building a few blocks away. She reappeared half an hour later, with Kerry and a suitably bandaged finger. Apparently the nurse over in A&E had said that we weren't to worry, animal bites are clean, it's usually only human bites where they need to worry about them

68

going septic!

I went back to school, after this, as I had intended. I had wanted to get back after chemo four, but due to all the messing about and problems that I had, I did not. I settled back into the routine at the San. I got up, I washed, I had breakfast, I did some work(!), programming, reading, drawing, listened to music, argued with Linda that computers weren't boring at all, etc., etc. It was a nice routine. It was during this period that I started to make leaps and bounds with the physio, and worked very hard at my exercises. Life in the San was OK, and I even started to escape occasionally to visit people, during the times when I did not have to be really careful of infections.

It was soon time for my (I thought at the time) last chemo, number six. The last chemo, time to celebrate, the end is nigh, and so on. Strange, but I wasn't keen to go. I was keen to have gone, though. Due to the timing of it, and the way things panned out, and the fact that it was half term just after my sixth chemo, and anyway, I wanted to celebrate, I came home after my last chemo, and we had a really good family week, and just enjoyed the fact that it was, as far as we knew at the time, over.

I went back to school after half term with a new goal: To get back to living in the house, with my mates. I was progressively walking further, and was doing a stupendous amount of physio, as I was seeing the school physio every day and doing my routine of exercises three times a day. Linda used to persuade me to go out on walks. We had to get me to the stage where I could walk far enough to manage a days walking between lessons before I could go back into normal school life. We managed it, eventually, with walks as far as the paper shop, and then into school, to visit the house. Steadily we rebuilt my stamina.

Mum and Dad also came down and took me out at the weekends. We got as far as the New Forest, where we wandered about and simply enjoyed the open air. We had a number of pub lunches and nice meals out, too.

I got back to living in the house just before the end of term. I started turning up to some lessons, and, most importantly, started playing catch-up with my work.

This being the Michaelmas half, there was the Soc Supper at the end of it - this is effectively the Christmas Party, but it is officially the feast in honour of the founder, Henry VI. It is traditional for the boys in a house to perform sketches after-wards, so Dave and I, and a couple of others, put together a sketch which was a perfectly sensible lecture on the principles of throwing custard pies. With practical demonstrations by lab coated and deadpan assistants. As you may be able to imagine, this went down rather well.

I had a check up at the hospital, a month or so after finishing the treatment. Pauline, a senior registrar and an exceedingly nice lady to boot, took my line out. It took her an awfully long time, as it had become well and truly embedded. Taking a line out is done under local anaesthetic, and it is just loosened at the point where it comes through the skin, and pulled out. Pauline was loosening for what felt like a week or two, but was in fact three quarters of an hour, and still it did not want to come out. She was all but kneeling on my chest and pulling, and I knew every ceiling tile intimately by the time that we were finished. How long a minute is very much depends on which end of the scalpel you are on. When it finally came out, I was very glad to get up off that bed, and to be rid of it.

Chapter 7 - A Levels

Well, from then on, I was a happy chappy. I thought that that was it, I was through, I was better, no more troubles, I had been left with a titanium leg, and a monstrously cool scar. Now all I needed to do was to attend the checkups, that would get less and less as time went on, until the five year all clear signal. This was it. This was the big time.

The end of term came, and the Christmas holidays started. I had been saving for some time to buy a computer, and now I had enough, and so I did. I had an excellent Christmas, as did all the family, and we generally lived it up a bit and celebrated. New year was equally good, and we had a few quiet drinks, had some friends round, and generally enjoyed ourselves some more.

When I went back to school, I was faced with the rather challenging task of catching up the work that I had missed in order to make some sense out of my A levels and Oxford application. I deliberated for a long time, and eventually decided to give up Design and just offer Double Maths and Physics. (Well, two-maths and an AS level extended further maths, really) This was backed up by the authorities as a good plan, and I just concentrated on those. That being said, I still had nearly two halves work to catch up. In Physics this was not a huge problem, as I had come across most of the work that was covered before under different guises, and in less detail, so it was merely boning up on subjects that I had covered before in a more rigorous way. However I had a great deal of Maths to do. I used the new found free time that I had, where before I had had Design lessons, to persuade various teachers to give up some of their time to me for catch-up lessons. This worked well, and I sort of absorbed by osmosis the rest of the material that I had missed, by learning the later material which used it and the groundwork at the same time.

I was disappointed to have to drop Design, as I genuinely enjoyed it, but there was no way I was going to have my course work finished on time and concentrate on the other A levels enough to get the grades I wanted. My Design project was fun, but I had all the theory and also a case study report to do, all of which counted towards the exam.

Anyway, the extra eight readers a week were very welcome.

At this time too, the hospital had rung me up and stated that they would be more comfortable if I came down to them and had some Radiotherapy, as a 'Belt and Braces job' as it was put. It was to make sure of no recurrence down in my leg. OK, I said.

It was explained that what was involved was a daily treat-ment of about ten minutes, every Monday to Friday for six weeks. I explained that that was a bit difficult, as I was trying to get my A levels on track right now, and how did they propose to work that, then, eh? Well, we got it figured out so that my treatment was late in the day, so I could commute into London each afternoon after lunch and simply miss my afternoon lessons, of which, due to the way my timetable now fell out, I only had two a week. Both Maths.

The radiotherapy was easy compared to the chemo. I went in, I lay on the table, I was lined up, they pushed the big red button, they ran away, the machine buzzed, they came back, I went home. That was about as complicated as it got. So, that was that.

One thing that this episode did convince me of, though, was that I did not want to be a commuter into London. They are a strange breed. They sit, or more usually, stand on the train, in a sort of half-world, an ethereal zone between home and the office, where their clothes are a mishmash of office wear, with maybe a jumper and rucksack slung over their shoulder. Or they don't stop working till they get home, they consider the train part of their office, their normal working day, and continue to scribble memos, or worse make calls to business associates, no doubt also on some train, riding home.

The mobile phone users annoy me. The mobile is a great invention, a giant leap in terms on communication ease, and it is a marvellously useful thing. But it is so often misused, by people in public places who think they are simply cool, and people who shout their conversations and bits of their private life out across the assembled masses, saying hey, look at me, I have a far cooler life than you because I own this phone.

There is a theory that mobile phones slowly frazzle your brain due to the microwave emissions from them. There is another theory that says, for the most part, this has already happened, and that's why mobile phone users tend to be loudmouthed, overbearing idiots who insist on making phone calls to tell people that they will see them in two minutes, rather than waiting two minutes to tell them personally. Such phones should come with an etiquette guidebook, that is forced reading, followed by a test, like the driving test. It should be illegal to make phone calls in an antisocial place.

Well, I settled down again into house life, and started to get

73

up to the usual things with Will, Dave, and the rest of the bunch. Having got to the upper sixth, life was more interesting, more free, and there were great characters from below us in the house. People like Chaz, with his inexhaustible supply of Star Trek books and Marvel Comics. Colin T. Troll, with his frenetic ginger hair, and slightly wild look on life. Ivo, whose acting skill never ceased to amaze me.

As a house, during the Lent Half, we put on a house play, called 'Doggs Hamlet, Cahoots Macbeth' which if I remember rightly is a Tom Stoppard effort. This was brilliant fun, as the plays revolve around the idea of a new and different language, Dogg, which uses the same words as English, with different meanings. So 'Gym shoes' means 'Excellent' and 'Brick' means 'OK'. This allows great scope for highly amusing scenes where one character who speaks English meets another who speaks Dogg, and they have a conversation which both understand, but differently. It's a very funny play, but demanding on the actors, and on the audience. I recommend it to anyone.

I spent the Easter holidays enjoying life (and doing a certain amount of revising (!)) The thing which concerned me about my exams was the Maths. I did not get on with my applied maths teacher, and neither did anyone else in my division. In particular, due in part to the fact that I had missed a lot of work and in part to the fact that I did not get on with his teaching style, I struggled with a lot of the harder mechanics he covered with us. Accordingly it was on this that I concentrated.

Up until half term in the summer, we were simply attending revision lessons, as we had finished the syllabus's for our various subjects at the end of the previous term. This was hard work, and everyone in the year really started to gear up for their exams. After half term, we were on study leave, and our only school commitments were chapel and exams. This left huge amount of time for relaxation, er, I mean, revision.

We spent our time between working just enjoying the summer. Unlike at day schools, where people leave at half term, and only come back for exams, we were at school all the time, but a boarding school without lessons is a great place to live, as you have an enormous amount of personal freedom to organise your time. That, along with the fantastic amount of work we had done before half term, meant we could spend the time relaxing, and as a result, we went into our exams well prepared, and not stressed about them.

Exams are funny things. Some people dread them, I rather like them. It is a culmination of the work, a finishing, and a final outpouring that marks the end of a course nicely. I refuse to worry about them. There is a great deal written about good exam technique, and how you should organise your revision. I usually found the best thing to do immediately before an exam is relax. I rarely did much work, the day before a major exam, as I take the view that if you don't know it by twenty four hours before hand, then you aren't going to learn it in a day. The thing that helped me most was simply doing practice papers. If you can do lots and lots of practice questions of the type that will come up then you are well away. Anyway, there is always the chance that the exam board recycle questions. It does happen occasionally that one comes along that is a thinly disguised rework of an earlier question from an earlier paper.

Towards the end of term, as most people had just about finished their exams, we had a number of parties and dinners and other social things, and finally, we 'Took Leave of the Headmaster'. This is a ritual where one goes to see him, one signs out of the school, in a similar fashion to signing in, and you receive a book of poetry, specially produced for this one use. And that, as they say, was that.

Chapter 8 - The Past Year

I left school on June 30th 1996. I had a check-up coming the following week, and Will and I had organised a trip to a major rock concert in Hyde Park. So, I went home for 48 hours, then trundled off to London, as the check-up was on the Tuesday. I had planned to stay with Will that week until the Concert on the Saturday.

Of course, the best laid plans...

The check up didn't. My chest X-ray showed pulmonary mestastetes, i.e. secondary growth in my lungs, or even lumpy bony bits where there didn't ought to be. It was explained that this was not good, and further treatment would be necessary. I was gutted. The worst had happened, I was back to where I had been, except this time around, I knew the significance of it all. I made a very difficult phone call to my parents that afternoon, to try to explain what was going on. They understood, but my message cannot have been very coherent. I knew that the first thing the hospital would want to do would be to make a few tests to check out what was what, then compile a set of results to figure out what to do next. Jeremy, the consultant, and I worked out between us that we could probably meet again for clinic the following week to sort things out. I persuaded Mum and Dad that I should stay down in London to have the tests done, and that I could come home as planned, and then travel down with them for the clinic. So I ended up stopping at Will's anyway, and went to the concert, (which was brilliant, by the way, as the players there were people like Bob Dylan and The Who and a number of other rather famous people). The best bit, though, was when it ended, and fifty thousand people tried to get into Lancaster Gate tube station at the same time. Duly, I went home on the Sunday, and came back with my parents to clinic on Tuesday.

In the clinic, it was explained that though this was serious, it was not as bad as it might be, as there were still plenty of treatment options available to us. The timing was not great, as it was running up to my birthday, and also Sue from the ward had been arranging a holiday for ex and current patients, and I had been down on the list for this. It was therefore decided to start treatment again shortly after my eighteenth birthday.

For my birthday, I was given a nice watch, and a bottle of very nice eighteen year old Whiskey. It was a reserved birthday, but fun nonetheless. For the next few days, people kept saying to me, does it feel any different, and I said, yes, I never used to have to answer daft questions about being adult.

The holiday was to the Lake District, to the National YMCA centre on the shores of Windermere. If you have never been to the Lake District, you have missed out, as it is an exceptionally fine area. I was not convinced of the idea, as I turned up, because out of the forty or so people in the group, only four were from our unit, and of those, I only knew Alan, the staff nurse who had come along. However, the ice was soon broken as people got to know each other. There was a fairly tight schedule of activities resulting in long days, and we did a phenomenal range of things. Amongst other things, we did orienteering around the grounds, canoeing on the lake, an assault course, and rock climbing. One of the highlights of the week was the raft race. We were split into four teams, one of which was made up from the nurses and other hospital staff who had accompanied the patients. Those who were fitter were hobbled by giving them less equipment. At the whistle, we assembled our own rafts, raced out around a buoy and back to shore. Except it wasn't that simple. The staff team's raft spent the whole time hanging about while its members attempted to undo the ropes on the other rafts. This led to the rafts tending to fall apart and dumping their cargo of people in the lake. All good clean fun.

Another particularly fine time was had on our overnight canoe bivouac expedition. We packed up our kit into several large open canoes, and set out in the afternoon up the lake. We paddled a mile or so up, and pulled in on a spur of land, and camped for the night. There were a number of very late night card games that went on, and some particularly good camp food cooked in the best tradition on a meths camp burner. The following morning, bright and early, we set off back to the centre at approximately 7am, and spent most of the trip singing Monty Python songs.

On the final evening, we were given transport up to a small town called Hawkshead, and we had a night out sampling the local pubs, of which there are many. The Lake District seems to specialise in interesting small towns with an exceptional range and quality of drinking establishments. I was so impressed with Hawkshead, that when my parents came with the rest of my family to pick me up the following day, we went back to Hawkshead and had lunch in another of its pubs. A good place indeed.

I came back, and went to hospital to have the drug that we decided on - Methetrexate. I had 3 lots of it, at weekly intervals. Immediately before this, we had received an extremely kind offer from Dr Gailey to use Manor house as a base during the first part of the summer holidays. So my Mum, siblings, and I stayed at Manor House while I had my methetrexate. I still cannot begin to understand how my dad managed. He stopped at home at work while we were away, and just came to visit at the weekend. Where he got the strength, I don't know.

I want to say at this point that throughout the time when I was in regular treatment, from the very beginning, right through to well after I had officially left the school, and in fact up to the present day, that the support from the school and associated people has been phenomenal, far more so than we could ever have conceivably anticipated. In particular, the constant phone contact and letters from the Gailey's, who have had some experience with such serious health problems, was of enormous help to me.

Press coverage of the school during my final year there had been very active. This was irritating, but inevitable, as the future heir to the throne was currently in the first year of the house. This meant a certain amount of tightening of security, but not half as much as I for one had expected, and, to be honest, it was quite nice in that he was treated in exactly the same manner as anyone else. The press were asked, after the initial excitement, to leave him to get on with school life, and by and large, they did so.

However, during the time that we were stopping at Manor house, one of the tabloids managed to get hold of that summers House Photo, and printed it as a centre page spread. No-one in the house, including all the staff, had a copy of this yet, as the photographers do not send it out until the following term, so it was quite nice to get a preview. It just would have been nicer to have had my copy before my picture was sprawled across the country's breakfast tables, that's all. My Mum was part way through her breakfast that morning, when the phone rang, and she received a nice call from the palace office, and could we get hold of Dr Gailey for them, please, as they would like him to know about this incident. Slightly stunned, my mum came back into the kitchen, and explained all to me. We went out and bought a copy, as it is not every day that you get you picture in the paper.

The Methetrexate at first worked well. I have a vivid memory of a certain senior registrar called Pauline hopping and skipping down the corridor with glee, clutching a film of my chest X-Ray, saying, come here, come here, look at this!

It wasn't as bad as the other drugs I have had, either, to have, and it did not really have many side effects other than knocking me for six and making me very, very, tired. We continued to get good results for three cycles, but then progress slowed up, and it stopped working so well. Cancer tends to evolve under pressure from a drug, and if it doesn't have enough of an effect to kill it quickly, it will become resistant. It is this fact that makes it so difficult to treat.

This was a great shame. We switched to using a combination of two more drugs, Iphosphamide and Etopocide. Well, I was just as ill, but not as sick, as with the first drugs. The first cycle that I had, I was fine right through, and I felt OK, and ate and slept well. I thought at the time this was too good to be true, and this was the case. It had a sting in the tail. I started to feel funny in the head, (some say no change there then) and it messed with my balance. On the evening before the day that I thought I was going home on, I had a bad faint in the bathroom. I blacked out. When I came to, there was a huge number of people round me, and my mum was squatting next to me holding my hand. I discovered I was on a mattress, on the floor in the bathroom, with numerous machines, some of which were going 'bing' occasionally. They had run a huge amount of some drug into me to try to raise my blood pressure which had dropped to very low indeed. Within about half an hour, I was lying in bed. They had used the opportunity to pull out all those bits of dusty medical equipment out of the back of the cupboard and see what they did. I had all sorts connected up, and I was carefully watched overnight. They investigated all the strange effects, and gave me a good going over, the following day, but nothing was found to account for the fall.

As you can imagine, it took a while to regain my confidence, and get up and move about. I don't like that bathroom to this day.

I had a number of cycles of this regime of chemo, and did not have any major problems, but I was ill. I was starting to get into trouble again with my blood counts, and I went into my local hospital at home, to have a blood transfusion. They have a day chemo unit, who were very well set up, and very efficient. I had the blood, and came home that night, and all was going well, until I started to feel unwell. My temperature went up, so we called the doctor. My temperature started to shoot, so we dialled 999 and said 'Help!!' I have a lot of respect for the ambulance service. I probably owe them my life that night. I was rushed into Accident and Emergency. The family who live across from us in our street, the Bougheys, came out to see if they could help. I was very, very, unwell that night. My mum and dad were with me all the way, talking, and keeping me awake. I had two of the largest canulas in my wrists that I have ever seen, and my mum tells me now that they ran an enormous amount of fluid into me in a very short time, along with some antibiotics and other exciting niceties. I spent the next couple of days recovering in bed. Once I was well enough, I was shipped to the Middlesex by ambulance as I was due to be going that week anyway for treatment. It took three and a half hours down the motorway. The ambulance men were great - they had just gone off shift when they got a call - Would they volunteer for a transport job to London? It is a credit to them that they did. I do remember needing to stop for bathroom facilities half way down and being wheeled out to the gents at a garage complete with drip and chair. The attendant wasn't quite sure what hit her, I think. It was certainly unusual.

I didn't know this at the time, but Mrs Boughey sat up all night baby-sitting my sisters. This is a prime example of the kind of continual background support that has been displayed by all the family friends and acquaintances. I may not have mentioned it, as I did not necessarily know about it at the time, or even afterwards, but there are hundreds of people who put themselves out over the last two years to try to make mine and my family's lives easier.

I arrived on the ward, and I proudly showed my canulas off to Julie (a staff nurse), who recoiled in shock. They really were huge. I asked her nicely, and she removed one of them, which meant I could use one of my hands more freely at last. They were a good two inches long, when we pulled them out. Yuck. By the time I finished my course of antibiotics, I was due for my chemo, and just at that stage, I really couldn't face it. We asked the consultant nicely to postpone it a further week, so we could go on holiday. So, we went home, and planned out a holiday. We had 4 days in a hotel in St. Ives, Cornwall. This was a fantastic holiday, and we had a wonderful time eating lots, spending lots, and generally making merry. St Ives is a wonderful place. We went at a time well out of the high tourist season, and as a result, it was quiet. We simply spent the time shopping around the place, which has a brilliant and very interesting range of shops, and doing the scenic bits, like standing on top of the cliffs heroically gazing out to sea (just in case we could glimpse America). You get the idea. We had a whale of a time.

However, I had to get back to the grindstone, and having come home again, I went back to the Iphos. This cycle was better, in terms of the problems, or lack thereof, but when the results came through from the regular scans, it showed a reduced effect. We held a council of war with the consultants. They offered us some ideas, and eventually we decided to take a break over Christmas, and to come back in January to decide on course of action then. I was to have a scan at the end of January to see, for example, whether an operation would be possible.

I had two months off. Everyone in the family by this stage was tired, and overwrought. We needed the time to regroup and give whatever was to come now our best shot. I spent the time re-establishing links with the real world, and doing some things of my own, and enjoying having a life that was not dictated by the hospital. It was valuable time.

During this period, I did a lot of programming, and finally wrote a computer game worth releasing onto the Internet, which I duly did. This was something I had wanted to do for a long time. It is called CrazyCar, and is a two-player car racing game for PowerMacs. I took the decision to donate all the proceeds to Sargent Cancer Care for Children. Amateur computer software can be released by a number of methods. It can be placed in the public domain, to be freely copied and distributed without any restrictions. You can also release it as shareware, which means it is freely copiable, but you are honour bound to pay the author his due. I ask that anyone wanting to keep it must send a donation to the charity. At the risk of plugging it further, interested parties should look for it on major archives of Mac shareware on the 'Net, for instance, on the Info-Mac archive.

That December, I was invited back to the house to go to Soc supper. I stopped over at Ian's house. Ian is another good friend of mine, and has the added distinction of being Mr Desborough's son. He's the same age as me, and someone I got to know very well, because he did precisely the same A levels in the same divisions, too, so I saw him for every taught period. Added to which, he now attends Lincoln College Oxford, on the same course that I was applying for at this time. Fortunately, he's a guy who's easy to get on with. Amongst other things, he owns a whole collection of guitars, six at the last count, which he plays regularly, and is an extreme Def Leppard fanatic. I don't hold it against him, though.

It was a bit weird to be a guest at my own house's Soc Supper, but I suppose it was not as weird for me as for Ian, to be a guest at another house's Soc supper. Nevertheless, it was an extremely enjoyable evening, and it was nice to see that few things had changed since we had left.

I also, around this time, had my Oxford interviews. I was told that I could stop the night beforehand if that would make life easier, and that I would have three separate interviews. I was applying to join Lincoln College, but one of the interviews for engineering was at Brasenose, this being allocated as my second choice. The other two were at Lincoln, one for Computation, one for Engineering.

I arrived at teatime on that Tuesday evening, and went to get my room and so on sorted out. At the evening meal, I met up with a group of other interviewees, and we decided to go out to sample the pubs around Oxford. After all, we needed to find out about the important considerations in our choice of further education establishment. This naturally resulted in me looking and feeling my best the next morning.

I had my three interviews in that one day. The first interview, Computation, was most reassuring. We talked for the most part about juggling, and a little about previous programming experience. Then he asked me a couple of cursory questions, that were easy, at least to anyone who can already program, and that was that. Cool, I thought, this was great. I had it made here. Well, the next interview was a bit more taxing. This was the Lincoln Engineering interview, and I was asked some nice questions, mainly mathematical. I had been asked to select two topics from a list, so I chose vectors, and differential calculus. I managed to muddle through without completely losing it, and actually, I think I did OK. The third interview was the disaster. I walked into the room, wearing my coat, as by this stage of the day, it was dark, and I was cold. I took this off, or at least tried to. Some how, I managed to get my elbow stuck in the shoulder, and I couldn't get my right hand out. There I was, frantically struggling in what now felt like a straight jacket, when the bloke stuck his hand out for me to shake. When I finally freed my hand, after some wild contortions that Houdini would have been proud of, I yanked my coat off, and its tail flicked round, taking with it about two dozen board markers from the shelf behind me. Added to which, it was a parquet floor so they bounced and rolled and clattered in all directions. Having got that little episode done with, we sat down, and I tried to answer the questions. Only, they were impossible. I couldn't see what he was driving at. By this stage, I was beginning to feel a little rattled. Anyway, eventually, he turned to my portfolio, and having gazed at the mighty works within, asked me some more impossible questions, just to put me at my ease. At last, after what now seemed to have been about three weeks, he said good-bye. I said good bye, picked up my coat, and my folio.

To find that the ring bindings had broken. The entire contents, a couple of dozen A3 sheets promptly did an extraordinarily good impression of a snowstorm.

I didn't want to go to Brasenose anyway.

I was supposed to get the results from these interviews just before Christmas. Unfortunately, there was an administrative mistake, and they sent them to number 14 on our street. We live at number 44. The inhabitants of No. 14 kindly sent it back to Oxford, and so in the meantime, I was left to wonder what my result was. I did not receive anything for a long time. Eventually I rang down to Oxford to see if I was getting a result, or whether I had done so badly they weren't going to bother telling me, not considering me to be worth the stamp. An extremely nice and slightly embarrassed lady on the other end of the phone told me that I had good news, and that they were going to offer me a place. I was a happy person. Of course, the next day, the posted results arrived, too.

However, the next thing on the agenda was my upcoming appointment down in London, to see what was what with my treatment...

During the week or so before the scan, I planned a visit to various places, as I was quite well, and I wanted to see them. I decided to start in London for the scan, then go on to Oxford for a few days, come back via Eton, then go back to London to meet my parents for the results.

After the scan, I set off, met Ian in Oxford, and met his mad friends, too. They are a really nice bunch of people who I managed to hit it off with in a very short space of time. We had a pleasant couple of nights, mostly in the bar, where the talk was mostly about parts of the country. It was nice to be in group of people who were from all over. We had myself and someone else from the Midlands, a couple from London, one from the South West, one from the North East, and so on. The exact position of the North/South divide has never been so hotly disputed.

I moved on to Eton, to see everyone there, and had a great time wandering around the place surprising people by turning up and disrupting things. I spent a pleasant morning being fed cups of tea, as everywhere that I went, I was offered one, and it is very hard to turn people down in that situation. By the end of the morning, I was awash with cuppas. I managed to get myself invited to join my House for lunch as a guest, which was nice, as I could talk to all the members of the year currently at the top of the house, who number among them some good friends.

Reluctantly, I travelled back down to London, and met Mum and Dad on the ward. The results of the scan were not good - I was basically inoperable due to the large number of problem areas. We had now also exhausted the list of conventional chemo drugs available, and there was little more to be offered.

I was given three choices. One was to do nothing. One was to do nothing for a bit, and then try option three, which was to try a trial drug called Docetaxel. After much deliberation I decided to wait for a bit, to do a few things that I really wanted to do, then to give it a shot.

We took time out, and came to the conclusion that the best thing to do with our time was to go on holiday to think things over. Eventually we decided to go to Somerset, as it was somewhere that we had never been to. I decided to do some visiting of my own, and so organised another trip around to Oxford and Eton. I persuaded my parents to drop me off in

Oxford when we came back.

Later in the same day that we decided to go to Somerset, James Pollard phoned me up, and invited me to his 18th birthday party, which was at his grandmothers house, and unfortunately, on the first night of our holiday. We ummed, and ahhed, until we suddenly realised that the party by some huge coincidence was about ten miles from where we were going anyway. One of life's little quirks.

It was a great party. A full Black tie do. There were 20-ish guests, mostly family members, none of whom I had met, apart from James' immediate family. Dinner was at eight, and it was excellent. We ate, drank, and made polite conversation for a long time, until Adrian appointed me Games Master, and asked me to organise some daft party games. I had a lovely time, persuading all the guests to make fools of themselves and we played some brilliant games that Adrian, James' dad, had thoughtfully briefed me on beforehand. One was a sort of cross between Chinese Whispers and Charades. This involves splitting the guests into two teams, one of which then leaves the room. The other team decides upon a charade, which they then act out to a member of the other team. Each member of the guessing team is then called in in turn, and has the charade acted to them by the previous member. The final member must declare what the charade was meant to be. This is usually hilarious. In the end, we didn't go to bed till 6am, when we realised the toddlers in the house, who had gone to bed before the party proper started, would be up in half an hour. I was dropped, half asleep, at the cottage we had rented for the week, the following afternoon.

We had a wonderful time for the rest of the week too, shopping, wandering about, and visiting various famous places. Somerset deserves its reputation for Cider, but there is an enormous amount of other cool things that we saw. One particular favourite was the Wookie Hole which is an extremely good set of show caves we visited.

At the end of the week I was dropped in Oxford. I had organised previously to meet a number of OE's (Old Etonians) in Oxford, as half of them are there anyway, and we went for a meal. To start with, we were going to have seven people, just OE's, but well, the party sort of, um, grew a bit as all of Ian's friends from his college came too, and we ended up with sixteen. We went to a great restaurant in the town, of which Oxford has many, and thoroughly enjoyed ourselves, in the way that students do.

I spent the next couple of days knocking about seeing people in Oxford, and then moved on.

It was during this visit to Oxford that I bought my guitar. I found a tiny guitar shop at the back end of Oxford, which sold me a basic steel-stringed acoustic guitar for 70 pounds.

Some of you out there may not understand my reasons for buying one. I was in a bad way, medically, I was not likely to survive, and I had never tried to learn an instrument before. There is a very old joke, that runs like this:

"Doctor, will I be able to play the piano after my operation?"

"Yes, why?"

"Oh good, because I couldn't before hand."

In deciding to learn the guitar, I am making a step towards coming out of these problems better than I went in. Being OK, getting better, beating the disease does not have to involve actually getting rid of it. That helps, of course. I am a better person than I was, and I am going to better myself, and not let the fact that I am dying rule my life. I can learn the guitar, and be in the situation where in going through the mess that is living with cancer, I can come out of it better off. That is one of the fundamental messages I want to get across in this book. Viewed from the right perspective, any bad situation can be used for good. It just takes a bit longer to find the perspective. It took me two years.

I had the drug that Friday. It was OK, it wasn't anything like as bad as the others I have had, as I was fine, and well, and OK until the following weekend. Then I got an infection, which I wasn't best pleased about, and ended up in hospital, in the North Staffs. Still, I managed to persuade them to let me out once my counts were up, which came up pretty quickly, and I took home some IV antibiotics, to be given in my line, so that was OK.

I organised to see Ian again after the second treatment, which was great, as we had tickets for the opening night of Star Wars, the revamped version. I got onto the ward at 2:15, and communicated that I needed to be away fast that evening. All I had to have was an hour long chemo infusion, and a chest X ray. Despite this, I didn't get away until 7:31. My cinema tickets were booked at Slough Cinema for 8:30. I made it across London, and out to Slough in record time. First, I got a taxi right outside the door to the hospital. Then I went to Paddington. I was wearing my Hat With Bells On at the time. The taxi driver asked me what the Hat was in aid of, so I told him. It was to bring a smile into peoples day. He asked if I had been doing charity work, and I said no, I was a patient. Oh, he said. So, by and by, as happens in taxies, he extracted my life story, and when we got to Paddington, he wouldn't take any money. He just said no, I deserved a good break, and anyway, he wouldn't like me to think that all London taxi drivers were the money grabbing devils that many people think they are. I said OK, if he was sure, then that was fine by me!

I then walking into Paddington in time to watch my train pulling out. Hmm. I hung around on Paddington station wondering what to do for twenty minutes until the 20:07 to Slough. I should add at this point that the journey was 18 minutes to Slough from Paddington. I arranged by phone to meet Ian at the station in Slough, as my train came in, and then we dashed to the Cinema. We had to circumvent the shopping centre as it had closed for the night, but still we made it with two minutes to spare. It was a great film.

I had no problems with infections this time, but the steroids I was also on to prevent certain side effects also made me ache, and caused insomnia. I had a rough weekend again.

But, that cleared up, and I had a pleasant enough week. I arranged to stop at Ian's house (again!) the night before the treatment, this time. I had also arranged to visit Will and Dave's house in Winchester which is where they were living while working during their year off before University, and stop there the night afterwards. Dave volunteered to drive up to Stoke with me, and stop the night here.

The third chemo was planned after a CT scan, and I had the scan results that same day. That chemo never happened. The scan results showed that the new drug wasn't having the desired effect, and that there was little point continuing with it. The decision was taken to stop all treatment, as really, we had run out of options.

All the different drugs that I had been on, all the radio-therapy, the surgery, both that performed, and that discussed and rejected, had come to this. We were stuck. There were no further options, and that was it.

It was not a good day.

I spent the next few days contacting people and deciding what to do with my suddenly rather precious time.

I went back to Eton again, and saw everyone there. I had a very civilised elevenses with Mr Jaques, and got myself invited to lunch in Manor House. Seeing these people was very important to me. I was not as well as I had been and this made the trip harder work than it had been, and I knew that it was entirely possible that I would not necessarily see some of these people again.

It was very hard for me to be ill. For a long time, I have been an autonomous person, free from a lot of restrictions. This was especially true because I had been living away from home for so long. Now I was no longer as independent, and I was not as well, and I could no longer just up and away and travel to the other end of the country to see people. The trip home from Eton was difficult, and I was very tired when I arrived.

I have since persuaded people to come to see me, or persuaded a lift out of someone. I have needed to slow down a bit, and take things as they come.

We decided it was time to take another break, to forget about our worries for a bit. The idea came to go on a narrow boat cruise, and to that effect, we hired a 60 foot narrow boat, which we decided to take up the Macclesfield Canal. This holiday was wonderful. It was effectively a week long pub crawl, visiting one a day, for a meal or whatever, and generally relaxing and seeing the world from a slower pace. Three miles an hour sounds eminently sensible. It certainly changed my views on traffic. When we came to towns, and decided to nip into the centre to get some supplies, we really noticed the noise and speed of the cars. We were convinced that they had not been travelling that fast before.

I started to go to church again, in the evenings. In our local parish the evening service is the one that my circle of friends attend. I would cadge a lift up to the church with my friends from across the road, Clare and Alison. I needed to get my thoughts straight on a few matters. I did not know where I stood. Going to church was something I had not done for a while. I have consciously led my life with as much personal integrity as possible and I was as close to the Christian moral ideal as I could personally get by my own efforts yet I was not actually sure of my beliefs. I figured a long time ago that I might as well use the moral code and teachings about the best way to live my life, and take the spiritual side on trust, until I had worked that out. I suppose that it's in the nature of the spiritual side of things, that you need to take it on trust.

I don't know why I started to go to church again. I suppose the impending uncertainty of my future triggered a need to find some answers and take a decision. For years I have been agnostic in the true sense, as in acknowledging that I don't know what to believe. I have spent a long time reasoning about such things.

I did, and do, believe in a God, and here is my reason:

The biggest piece of evidence for a God in the first place is the World. There has always been an argument between the secular scientist and the religious as to the lack of evidence in the sciences for any of the religious tenets. I think this is rubbish, and the people who make such arguments are blind to something very basic. If you credit a God with divine intelligence, then He will naturally come up with a pretty damned fantastic plan and design for a universe. Such systems as natural selection and evolution are so brilliantly simple yet give rise to such mind blowingly complex life forms and ecosystems as we have on this little blue planet, that they could

94

only have been thought of by a divine intelligence. Man would think, in his limited wisdom, that to create a universe is very hard, and it needs some very complex planning. God would just think of a way to start the thing and let it create the complicated bits automatically. This is borne out by the science we have discovered. When man finally figured out that the sun was in the centre of the solar system, the picture of the solar system got lots more simple. Before, there needed to be loops in the orbit of Mars and all sorts of complex mechanisms to keep the planets moving in the way that they do from our view point. We are only just probing the edges of knowledge, and we have explained a great many things, but the more we find out, the simpler the picture gets. Stephen Hawkins has proven, he says, that the total energy in the universe is zero, if you count the potential gravitational energy between matter as being negative (an intuitive step if you know any physics) This has the convenient side effect that you don't have to violate the law of conservation of energy to create a Universe, which strikes me as good evidence that whoever made it thought long and hard. People who deny the existence of God on scientific grounds are too close to their specific details. Stand back and the fact that the whole is simple stares out at you like a neon sign saying 'God is here' People studying the letter 's' in the word 'is', cannot see that.

I went to a service where I was anointed with oil for healing, and had a number of people pray with me. This was not a light decision and it was not a statement of belief from me. It was a statement of open-mindedness, and of a desire to find belief because it was what I believed, not what others around me wanted to believe I believed. I needed to know that if I took a decision to believe one thing or another, it was me that took that decision. For the correct reasons for me.

95

The definition of a good service, by my reckoning, is one which you take away something that you didn't arrive with. It was a good service. I took away a realisation that there was a God. I had believed there was for ages, but it was the difference between believing something to be true, and having personal experience of a true, gut, belief of something that you really believe and trust in. That is what was missing before. I will use the terms belief, and faith, to distinguish. Belief is something you have in the head, something that you can arrive at by logic, and study. Gut Belief, Faith is something that you just have to go for and accept. You must accept that something is really true, that you can trust a premise as you would a fact. They are two different things, and the English language could do with two different words to describe two different things.

Since then, I have been thinking a lot about Christianity, and Religion more generally. I needed to make a decision about what I really think. For an awfully long time I ran around in circles. I argued this way and that, I wrote essays, I even won a year prize for one that I wrote in the Lower Sixth. I was gobsmacked, after all, I am a Scientist and Mathematician by my qualifications. My worst results were in the arts subjects. Since when could I write essays?

I have come to the conclusion that I needed to stop arguing it out. I had been through the standard arguments. I know the usual explanations of this and that, and that I think is the problem. For Christianity to be worth it, it has got to have happened as we are told it did. Explaining this miracle and that away, and trying to show how the resurrection could have happened is pointless. In the end, you just have to accept it. It is such a simple step, and I still have difficulty with it.

Part of my difficulty is that Christianity is free. You don't need to do anything to earn it. It means that you need to accept that you are worth it, and that is awfully difficult. All that it requires to become a Christian is a commitment from you to Jesus Christ our Lord. This commitment involves two things. One is to say sorry for your sins and accept that they have been removed and forgotten, and to use the bridge of Jesus Christ to reconcile yourself with God. Jesus did the hard bit, two thousand years ago. The other is to trust God with running your life. He will make his Will known, you need to be receptive to that.

Revelations chapter three verse twenty reads as follows: "Behold, I stand at the door and knock; if anyone hears me and opens the door, I will come in and eat with him, and he with me." To become a Christian, I needed to open the door. I had a lot of problems with doing this. For example, I was worried about people. A lot of people I know had been praying for me, and praying that I would find Christ. I was afraid that if I did go ahead and make a commitment, they would get very excited, and go leaping and jumping about, and generally be very enthusiastic and so on, which I did not want, I did not want the attention. This may sound daft, but I was shy!

Another, much bigger problem I had, was that actually, I did not want to come out and say, yes, I've done it, I'm a Christian, and then in two weeks time discover that I wasn't. I wanted to make a commitment and keep it. I didn't know if I could. I got around this obstacle by realising this: Part of making a commitment is trusting Christ to help you keep it.

However, I have made a commitment. On June 5th, 1997, I prayed a prayer of commitment and repentance for my sins with a member of the ministry team from up at the church. I did this finally, because I realised there had been a lot of knocking. I have just not necessarily heard it. The Lord God is nothing if not persistent. I also came to the conclusion that I was dithering, and finding excuses not to. If I hadn't have come to a decision soon, I wasn't going to be able to. So I came to a decision.

I went round to my friends, and had a nice cuppa, and talked about this and that, and tried to think of some more excuses, and couldn't, and eventually gave up, and went for it.

The release was wonderful. The burden of indecision was lifted. The knocking stopped, and quiet came. In the day or so running up to this, I had not been able to get the topic off my mind - I had been constantly thinking about the decision I had to make, and weighing this up, and arguing the other, and now I had landed on one side of the fence and all I had to worry about now was keeping my promise. And I have the Lord's help with that.

Epilogue

There are a number of points to this book. It is not my place, as author, to tell you what they are. It is my place to write the book, and let you draw your own conclusions about things. English teachers everywhere understand this.

I want to get a few people to think, to observe, and to do their best to live. I cannot remember who said it, but there is a fine quote from some film or other... "Every man dies, but not every man really lives" ... I think that this is very true, and that people should strive to live, in the best way that they can, and to achieve something in their own eyes.

People ask me, am I OK? and I say yes. They look at me as if I am a bit funny in the head, but I am. There has been a continual process of healing going on for a long time. Of course, a lot depends on what you understand by healing. There are two sorts, spiritual, and physical. The passage through the times that I have had and my illness, has stripped away the unnecessaries, and left me. I am a better person for it, but I still have room for improvement. As I have already pointed out, beating my disease does not need to include getting rid of it. It would have been nice.

I have a faith that I did not have before I wrote this book. My experiences have forced me to look at my life again, and try to understand it. I have had belief in the head for a long time, but only recently have I experienced belief in the gut.

The 'good' services I have been to in the last few weeks have shown me that yes, the God I always believed ought to exist, for head reasons, does really exist, and he does move in mysterious ways. You get help, but usually what you need, not what you wanted or expected, and sometimes in a form that you would not recognise if you weren't looking at the problem in the right way. I have had a lot of help all though my life and only recently did I realise that fact.

We'll see where I go from here, then, shall we? The journey has been pretty interesting so far.